LEGENDS
OF IRELAND

LEGENDS
OF IRELAND

By J. J. Campbell

With drawings by Louis le Brocquy RHA

B. T. BATSFORD LTD

LONDON

First published 1955
Reprinted 1987
© J. J. Campbell 1955

ISBN 0 7134 5823 2

Printed in Great Britain
by Biddles Ltd, Guildford
for the publishers,
B. T. BATSFORD LTD
4 Fitzhardinge Street, London, W1H 0AH

FOR MY WIFE
WHO HELPED

CONTENTS

INTRODUCTION

A BOOK of this size can contain no more than a selection from the multitude of legends and tales which are preserved in the literature and folk-lore of Ireland. The present collection contains some that are well known, some not so well known, and some which have not, to my knowledge, been included in any published collection before. I have retained one or two old favourites, and have rejected a number of old favourites. I have made little substantial change in the tales as they are found in the Irish of published texts, but have in many cases condensed the narrative to greater or less degree.

Whatever the merits of the versions given here, I have given them as stories, not as sources of any branch of history, not as subjects of academic study. My only regret is that in trying to keep fairly strictly to the main narrative of the stories I have had to reject those deviations from the main theme, in both prose and verse, in which the ancient story-teller and, one feels, his audience, so obviously found such keen enjoyment; and in order to include all the tales of my choice I have had to dispense with some of the rich detail in descriptions of persons and places and nature which, though stereotyped to a great extent, is nevertheless a peculiar and

1

proper part of the Irish story-teller's manner and art, and indicative of a keen appreciation of the emotional significance of natural beauty.

The tales fit roughly into three groups, the first of which is on a near-epic plane and is concerned with Ulster of the times of Cuchulainn, and centres around Conor Mac Nessa and the warriors of the Red Branch and Cuchulainn himself, the "little black-browed" hero, son of a god, fated to a short life packed with wonder and glory from infancy; the second group, which comes at the end of this collection, belongs to a more popular cycle and is concerned with Finn and his son Oisin and the other warriors of the Fian; and the third group concerns various heroes, heroines, kings, queens and clerics. In all three groups the peoples of other worlds move and live naturally, the supernatural Tuatha De Danann, the great god Dagda, Lu and Angus Og of the fairy fort of the Boyne, the ever-young people of the lands of youth and promise, and the little folk, the leprechauns of the folk-tales. The last of these have a tale to themselves, *Eisirt*.

A feature of many of the stories is a kind of deprecatory self-consciousness on the part of the narrator which finds expression occasionally in a mild burlesque of his own art or in the touch of humour even in the most tragic tale. One tale in the collection, *The Demon of Gluttony*, is conceived entirely as a burlesque of the heroic legend and the pious life of the saint. In the Ulster cycle, *Bricriu*, and in the Finn cycle, *The Hard Man* and *The Clown in the Grey Coat*, and in the miscellaneous group part of the tale of *Brian Boru's Son* exhibit the humour of the ancient story-teller.

My intention, however, in introducing the collection was not to draw attention to those qualities in the tales which to me made them worthy of yet another presentation in English, but rather to let the tales show in themselves the eternal drama which makes one feel that with but little change of circumstance the people in them could be the people of our times raised to greatness.

My acknowledgments, in the making of the collection, are first the acknowledgments of all who have approached the legends of Ireland as amateurs, to the great company of scholars of other days who worked over the old Irish manuscripts and the texts based on them, to the contributors to the pages of *Revue celtique*, *Irische Texte*, the *Transactions of the Ossianic Society* and *Eriu*, to the *Todd Lecture Series* and the *Irish Manuscript Series* of the

Royal Irish Academy, to Standish H. O'Grady's great *Silva Gadelica*, to the publications of the *Irish Texts Society* and the Irish Stationery Office, Dublin.

For advice and assistance in the preparation of the volume my thanks are owing to those who so freely, after the manner of all librarians whom I have ever met, made available to me the resources of the library of the Queen's University of Belfast, the Linenhall Library, Belfast, and the Belfast Public Library's Reference Department, especially Miss A. Hackett, Deputy Librarian of Belfast, and Mr. R. Jenkinson; to Mr. Sam Hanna Bell of the B.B.C., Belfast; to Mr. Walter Crozier, of Messrs. Mullan's, Belfast; to Dr. Padraic Gregory, F.R.I.B.A., who read the proofs; to Miss K. Palmer, who typed the script.

CHAPTER I

Becuma

CONN the Hundred-Fighter was king of Ireland, and while his queen, Eithne, daughter of the king of Norway, lived, he ruled well, so that the country was prosperous and contented. But when Eithne died he could find no peace, nor could he turn his mind to the government of his kingdom.

One day he was so overcome with his grief that he went from Tara alone to Ben Edair, there to weep and lament for his wife and queen.

And at the same hour judgment was being passed by the Tuatha De Danann in the Land of Promise on the woman Becuma because of the sin she had committed with Gaidiar, son of Manannan Mac Lir. The judgment was that she should be either burned or banished, according to the decision of the council. The council consisted of her father, Eoghan Invir, and Gaidiar's father, Manannan, and Gaidiar and Ilbrec, sons of Manannan, and Lodan, son of Lir, and Gae Gormsuileach and Fergus Findliath. Manannan

5

said: "Banish her; for if we burn her, the requital will fall upon us and upon the Land of Promise." So to Ireland they banished her, for the Tuatha De Danann hated the Irish, who had driven them from the surface of Ireland.

Now Becuma loved Art, son of Conn the Hundred-Fighter, though Art did not know of her love: so she was glad that her banishment was to Ireland. And she sped in her coracle that needed no rowing, over the seas, until she came to land at Ben Edair, where she saw and recognised the king. And Conn saw her coming, fair-skinned, yellow-haired, with black eyebrows, grey eyes, snow-white teeth and thin red lips; alluring to look upon as she walked towards him, clad in green, red and gold. He ceased from his lamenting and asked her name and her dwelling.

"I am from the Land of Promise," she answered, "and my name is Delbchaem, daughter of Morgan. I am come in quest of Art, the high king's son, whom I have loved from afar."

"I would not come between you and the man of your heart," he said; "though I myself have no wife."

"Why have you no wife?"

"My wife is dead."

"Would you have me sleep with you then, instead of Art?"

"You must choose."

They made a pact then, that she go with the king to Tara, on condition that he sent Art away from Tara for a year. The condition grieved the king, but he consented: and Becuma hid her coracle in the rocks, in case she should need it again.

At Tara, Art was playing chess, with Conn's druid, Cromdes. Art moved a piece and the druid said: "That is a move of banishing. You will be banished because of the woman your father brings with him."

At that moment Conn and Becuma arrived and Conn told his son of the pact he had made. And the men of Ireland thought it unjust that Art should be banished because of a woman; but Art left that night.

For a year Conn and Becuma lived at Tara and during that time there was neither corn nor milk in Ireland. And the druids of Ireland came together at Tara and out of their wisdom and lore they judged the cause of the disaster to be the wickedness of Becuma. When they were asked how the country might be delivered from the evil, they replied that the son of a sinless couple must be

6

brought to Ireland and slain at Tara, and his blood be mingled with the soil of Tara. Conn, hearing this, said he would go in quest of such a boy, leaving his kingdom to Art while he should be away. And he bade Art remain at Tara until he returned.

First Conn went to Ben Edair and found the coracle. In it he travelled over the sea for six weeks, moving from island to island in his quest, and monsters and beasts of the sea rose up around him, and the waves rose in mountains and the universe trembled. But he was not daunted, but came at length to a beautiful island, where fair sweet-smelling apple trees greeted him, and hazel trees with golden-yellow nuts on them clustered round wells of sweet wine, and bees hummed busily among fair flowers and fruits. Near by he saw a well-made hostel, thatched white, yellow and blue with birds' wings. Its door-posts were of bronze and its doors of crystal. And entering he saw there the queen, Rigru Rosclahan, daughter of Lodan of the Land of Promise, and wife of Daire Degamra, son of Fergus Fialbrahach, from the Land of Wonders. There too he saw their son Segda Saerleorai, a lovely little boy, seated on a chair of crystal.

Conn went to the bed of the hostel and sat down; and his feet were washed, but he saw no one wash them. And a flame sprang up on the hearth, but he saw no one kindle it. And tables laden with many kinds of meats rose up before him, and a drinking horn was placed to his hand. Then the dishes were removed and he saw before him a vat of crystal: and Daire bade him go into the vat and bathe so that he might put away the weariness from him. After he had bathed a fair cloak was thrown over him and he slept.

When he awoke food and drink were set before him. He said he was under *geasa* not to eat by himself: and they said that none of them ever ate with another of them.

"I will eat with the king," said the boy, "so that he may not violate his *geasa*." And they ate and the boy remained with him.

In the morning he told them he had need of them. "Ireland is without corn or milk for a year," he said.

"What do you need of us?" they asked.

"Your son," he replied. "We have been told that through him our deliverance will come."

"Alas, not for the dominion of the world could we lend our son," they said.

9

"It is wrong not to accede to the king of Ireland's wish," spoke the boy. "I will go with him."

"Do not say it, son," they pleaded.

"The king of Ireland must not be refused," said the boy.

"If you must go, then," they said, "you will go under the protection of the kings of Ireland, and of Art, son of Conn, and Finn, son of Cool, and the artists of Ireland."

"As far as it lies in my power," said Conn, "it shall be so."

In three days and three nights the coracle took them to Ben Edair and they went immediately to Tara, where the men of all Ireland were assembled. The king placed the boy under the protection of himself and Art and Finn and the artists and the men of Ireland: only himself, however, and Art and Finn would accept the charge, and they were horror-stricken at the thought of slaying the boy. But the druids came forward and pronounced again their opinion with regard to the boy, that he should be slain and his blood mingled with the blighted earth and the withered trees that they might have life again. Then the boy stepped forward and said: "Men of Ireland, since it is your will that I be slain, leave me by myself in peace. Let me be slain as I shall say."

At that moment the lowing of a cow was heard and the wailing of a woman. They all turned and saw a woman drive before her a cow, and the two sides of the cow bulged into bulky bags. She drove the cow towards them and through their midst, until she stood by the king. Then she sat between Conn and Finn and asked was it true that the druids advised the slaying of an innocent boy though he was under the protection of Conn and Finn, and on being told that it was true, she asked: "Where are these druids?"

The druids came forward.

"Let the cow be slain," said the woman, "and her blood mingled with the soil of Ireland. Let the boy be spared. When the cow is cut up you will find in each of the bags on her sides a bird, one having twelve legs, the other one leg."

The cow was slaughtered and its blood mingled with the soil of Tara, and the birds were taken out.

"Let the birds fight," said the woman, "so that we may see which is the stronger."

They fought and to the wonder of all the one-legged bird was the victor.

"Now" said the woman, "the boy is the bird with one leg and the men of Ireland the bird with twelve legs. But the boy has right on his side and he is the victor."

And Conn recognised her as the boy's mother, and she led the king away from the others and advised him: "Send away Becuma, the woman of sin. It was for her sin that she was banished from the Land of Promise."

"If only I could," he said. "But I cannot. I am pledged."

"For as long as she is with you, then," said the woman, "Ireland will be without one-third of its corn and its milk." And she went off with her son, refusing all the precious gifts they would have given her.

Shortly after this Art was playing chess, and Becuma, looking out from the palace, espied him. Calling one of the men, she said: "Tell Art I place him under *geasa* to play chess with me for a prize at the choice of the winner."

So the board was fetched and they played, and Art won.

"I place you under *geasa*," he said to Becuma, "not to take food in Ireland until you find and bring to me the soldier's baton which Cu Roi Mac Daire held in his hand when he won Ireland and the world."

Becuma looked for help in her quest to the fairy communities, but found none until she came to her foster-sister Aine, and Aine told her where the baton was, in the stronghold of Cu Roi Mac Daire, on the top of Slemish, and how to obtain it. And she brought it to Art at Tara.

They played then a second game; but in this Becuma had the help of the fairy-folk, who stole Art's pieces from the board; and he lost the game.

"I win," she said.

"Not you but the fairy-folk," he said. "What is your prize?"

"I place you under *geasa*," she answered, "not to take food in Ireland until you find and bring here Delbchaem, daughter of Morgan."

Art set out in his coracle over the sea, and passed one island after another until he came to an island which attracted him by its luxuriant beauty. Here he landed and spent a long time gazing at the trees and the brightly coloured birds, and breathing the fragrance of the flowers, while he watched bees moving among

them, and listened to their humming mingled with the singing of
the birds.

Then in the middle of the island he espied a well-made house,
thatched white and purple with birds' wings, and going to it he
was welcomed by Creide Fiarlainn and her company of beautiful
women. They asked his name and he told them; and she fitted on
him a cloak which was ornamented with gold of Arabia. It fitted
him well. And she said: "Yes, you are the king of Ireland's son;
we have been expecting you"; and kissed him three times.

He stayed there six weeks, and marvelled every day at the
beautiful crystal bower and the vats which never emptied no
matter how often the water was taken away. At the end of the
month and a fortnight he told her of his quest, and she directed
his journey, telling him of the perils ahead, the great, dark ocean,
the fearsome wood, the water full of monsters, the mountain path,
the house at its end where the seven hags waited for him with a
bath of molten lead; and then the black-toothed Ailill, Morgan's
son, whom no weapon could hurt; and her own two sisters, with
two cups in their hands, one of poison, one of wine, of which he
must drink the one on his right, if need be; and at the end of it all
he would see the fortress, with a wall of bronze around it, where
the girl he sought was held, guarded by her mother, long-headed
Doghead, daughter of the king of the dogheads. And Morgan was
the girl's father, and her name was Delbchaem.

Thus directed, he set out, and slew the sea monsters, and escaped
the hags though they hacked him all the night through, and came
to the poisonous mountain of ice, and the glen of venomous toads,
and the long-maned lions of the mountain, and the river of ice,
where he met the giant Curnan, who was grinding his teeth on a
pillar-stone, and slew him, and after him met Morgan's son, Ailill,
whom no weapon could hurt, so that he needs must wrestle with
him; and him too he overcame, snapping his head from his neck.
And Ailill's wife, in terror of his threats, directed him on the last
stage of his journey to the fortress of long-headed Doghead, the
wife of Morgan.

Now she had been told by her druids that if anyone succeeded
in wooing her daughter, she herself would die. So she killed everyone who came to woo her daughter, and all around the bronze wall
of her fortress were poles, and on top of them were the heads of
those she slew. There was one empty pole, and that was intended

to hold the head of Art. It was Doghead who had set all the perils in his way, and she now waited for him, with the foster-sisters of Creide, holding their cups of poison and wine.

There was another waiting for him also, in her bower set on top of a pillar. She was endowed with chastity and beauty and wisdom: she had long golden hair, and raven-black eyebrows, and snow-white skin, and over her comely figure's elegant raiment a green cloak caught by a gold brooch at the throat.

When Art came she went into a house apart and waited with her maids; and she said to them: "There has come here today a warrior whom none in the world can surpass in form or fame. Bring him to the bower."

Art went into the bower and the maids welcomed him and washed his feet. Then came the sisters with their drinking cups, but Art remembered Creide's instructions. In a little while Doghead arose and put on her armour and called a challenge to Art. And he arose and fought with her and snapped off her head as he had done with Ailill, and placed it on the empty pole. Then he took Delbchaem to be his wife, and all that night there was feasting in the fortress.

But Morgan, who was away, returned in the morning full of anger at the slaying of his wife, and challenged Art, who, donning his armour, went to meet him. Heroic and fair he appeared in his helmet of dark gold, his glittering bronze apron over his satin tunic, with his two heavy spears and his shining sword, blue-hilted, broad-grooved, in his hand, and his great bossy shield over his shoulder.

The two met, like two huge stags in mortal combat, or two lions, or two mountainous waves of destruction, and Art vanquished Morgan, as he had vanquished the giant Curnan, and Morgan's wife, Doghead. Thus did he conquer the Land of Wonders and gather all its wealth to give to Delbchaem.

When Art and Delbchaem set out for Ireland a company went with them from the Land of Wonders. They touched Ireland at Ben Edair. Here Delbchaem remained and sent Art on ahead to Tara so that he might tell Becuma to leave at once. And Art was welcomed affectionately by all save the sinful wanton Becuma. Her he commanded to leave Tara, and weeping she went. And thus did Delbchaem come to Tara.

CHAPTER II

The Dream of Angus Og

ANGUS OG of Bru na Boinne was sleeping one night when a maiden appeared to him. In his dream she stood at the side of his bed, and he thought her more beautiful than all the maids of Ireland. He put out his hands to her, to take her to him, but she was gone before his hands could touch her. He woke with a start, and the vision was still clear in his mind, and he could not sleep again for thinking of her.

All next day his mind was uneasy and he was unable to eat; and when night came he fell asleep in weariness. His dream came again. This time the maid had a timpan in her hand and she played and sang to him. And his spirit was rested. But when he awoke again he was uneasy and restless and longed for the maid.

She came again to him next night, and every night for a year. He fell deeply in love with her, and in his waking moments he pined for her, so that he fell ill. They brought the physicians of all

14

Ireland to him, but they had no cure for him: for he did not tell them of the maid of his dreams.

But Fergne the physician of Conn was brought to him at last, and he knew when he saw him that his illness was of his mind. So sending everyone away he spoke to Angus in secret and said:

"Your sickness is a sickness of love."

"My sickness has betrayed my secret love," said Angus.

"Tell me," said Fergne.

"The most beautiful maid in all Ireland, she is," said Angus; "and every night for a year she came and sang and played her timpan. But I see her, alas, only in my dreams."

"If there is a remedy," said Fergne, "your mother, Boann, will find it."

So they sent for Boann, and Angus told her of the maid of his dreams. Boann at once ordered a search of all Ireland to find a maid like the maid of his dreams. But though they searched for a year, they did not find her. And Angus still pined away.

Fergne then sent for the father of Angus, the great Dagda.

"What can I do for his illness," said the Dagda, "when you have failed?"

"You are fairy king of all Ireland," said Fergne, "and a command from you to Bodb, the fairy king of Munster, will cause a search that will find the maid if she is to be found in Ireland."

The Dagda went to Bodb and told him of the illness of Angus and its reason. Bodb undertook the search, and he too searched for a year. At the end of the year, as agreed between them, the Dagda went to Bodb and asked him:

"Have you news for me?"

"I have," said Bodb.

"Is it good news?" asked the Dagda.

"I have found her," said Bodb. "She is at Lough Beal Draguin, at the harp of Cliach. Let Angus come and see if he recognises her."

So they set out for the lough, and there were one hundred and fifty maidens there. There was a chain of silver between every two maidens and necklaces of silver on their necks. And one was taller than the rest and she wore a necklace of shining gold. Angus knew her as the maid of his dream.

"Do you know her name?" he asked Bodb.

"She is Caer," he replied, "daughter of Ethal Abnual of the

fairy fort of Uaman in the province of Connacht. But you cannot take her now."

So they went to the Dagda and Boann at Bru of the Boyne and consulted together.

"It is best to go to Maeve and Ailill of Connacht," said Bodb, "and ask for the maid for Angus. For she is from their territory."

The Dagda went to Ailill and Maeve, and was welcomed by them, and they feasted for a week in celebration of his coming. Then the Dagda told the purpose of his visit.

"We have no power over her," said they.

"Send for the king, her father," said the Dagda. That was done. Ethal Abnual refused to come, for he knew why they had sent for him.

"I will not give my daughter to the son of the Dagda," he told the messengers.

Ailill marshalled his warriors, and together with the army of the Dagda they marched on the fairy fort of Uaman, and destroyed it and made captives of all in it.

"Now," said Ailill to Ethal Abnual, "give your daughter to Angus."

"I cannot," said Ethal Abnual, "for there is a power over the maidens which is greater than mine."

"Explain that," said Ailill.

"They are in the form of birds one year and in human form the next," said Ethal Abnual. "The maid you seek will be in the shape of a bird next summer at Lough Beal Draguin, and there will be one hundred and fifty swans with her. You may find her there if you wish."

After this there was friendship between the king of the Connacht fairies and Ailill and Maeve. And the Dagda went back to Bru of the Boyne and related what he had been told of the maid.

Angus went the following summer to the lough and saw the swans with silver chains between them two and two, and one with a golden chain taller than the rest. He was in human shape. He stood at the lough side and called to her:

"Come to me, Caer."

"Who calls?" she asked.

"Angus calls you," he replied; "come and yield to me in honour."

16

She came. He put his two hands on her as he had tried to do when he first saw her in his dreams. He took the shape of a swan then, and went round the lough three times with her. Then they flew to Bru of the Boyne, and their happiness together was such sweet music that those who heard it fell asleep for three nights and days.

The maid stayed at Bru of the Boyne; and it was in gratitude for bringing them together that Angus took the side of Ailill and Maeve in the great cattle raid of Cooley.

CHAPTER III

The Weakness of the Ulstermen

CRUNNCHU was wealthy and prosperous, living in the lonely hills with his wife and four sons. His wife died, and for years he and his sons lived without a woman in the house. One day a young woman, dignified and beautiful, came to the house and sat down by the fire. She said nothing, and Crunnchu watched her, silent also, as she rose again and set about the duties of a housewife, preparing food, milking the cows, directing the servants.

When night came she went to Crunnchu and he spoke to her then:

"Will you be my wife?"

"On condition that you speak my name to no one nor tell aught to anyone about me," she replied. And so it was agreed between them. They lived happily together, and with her his prosperity increased.

One day he told her that he was going to one of the great

assemblies of the men of Ulster, where there would be races and games and entertainments and combats. She begged him not to go.

"You may by accident speak of me," she said, "and I am very happy here with you, and would not like to leave. But our union is at an end if you speak of me to anyone."

He would not heed her; but assured her vehemently that he would not endanger their union by one word. And it was a glorious day of entertainment. In all the contests of chariot-racing the horses of the king were victorious, and the mouths of all the people were full of praise for them. And the poets sang the praises of the king and his wife. And they praised the horses, saying:

"No two such horses have ever been seen. Their speed could not be matched anywhere."

But Crunnchu, provoked by all the praise, and forgetting his promise, shouted:

"My wife could run faster than the horses you praise."

The king was enraged and cried out:

"Seize the man who said that."

The attendants seized Crunnchu and brought him to the king.

"Now," said the king, "you will prove that boast or pay for it." And he sent messengers to bring the man's wife at once to the assembly. Meanwhile Crunnchu was kept in bonds until his wife should be brought.

The messengers went to his house, where they were welcomed by the woman. When she inquired why they had come to her they said:

"Your husband has boasted to the king, in the presence of the whole assembly, that you can run more swiftly than the horses of the king. And he will not be released until you come to the assembly."

"My husband," said she, "spoke rashly. I am unwell. I am expecting a child."

"Your husband will pay with his life for his boast," said they, "if you do not come."

She demurred no more, but went with them. The great crowds in the assembly gathered round her and gazed at her. She was humiliated and embarrassed before them all and protested:

"It is not fitting that one such as I should be before all men's gaze. Say quickly what it is you wish of me."

"To race against the horses of the king," they all shouted; and there were cries of mockery and jeering.

She drew back. "But my time is near," she said. "I cannot do this."

"Very well," said the king. "Your husband dies." And he ordered his attendants to draw their swords.

She cried out in great distress: "Will no one help me?" She looked round the mob: "A mother bore each one of you. Have you no pity for me?" She turned to the king and begged him: "Give me but a short respite, until my deliverance is come, and I will do what you ask me."

"You run now, or your husband dies," he replied.

"For this shame you put upon me," she cried, "you and all your people will pay, in years to come."

The king ignored this, but ordered her to tell her name, before the race began.

"My name, and my offspring's name," she said, "will be on this place of assembly to mark the great shame of your deed today. I am Macha. And my descent is from Ocean."

She called for the horses to be brought, and she outran them to the end of the course; and her time came; and her twins were born. So the name Emain Macha.

All who were there felt a strange weakness on them, a weakness like hers in her pain. And she spoke to them a prophecy:

"The shame you have put upon me will be punished in each man of you. When crisis or danger is nigh to you, this weakness you feel now will come upon you, and upon your children to the ninth generation."

Her word was true. For though the weakness came upon the men it did not affect the women or children of Ulster, nor did it affect any men but those of Ulster, nor did it affect Cuchulainn, who was begotten of Lu. And that is why Cuchulainn stood alone against the warriors of Maeve, because of the weakness put upon the men of Ulster by Macha.

CHAPTER IV

Deirdre

CONOR MAC NESSA, king of Ulster, came once with the warriors of the Red Branch to the house of Feilimi his bard, and a great feast was set before them, so that they ate and drank and listened to tales and songs and music until they were heavy and sated and full of sleep. And first among those who attended on them through all the hours of their entertainment was the wife of their host Feilimi, even though she was heavy with child and near her time. When therefore the king and his warriors went drowsy to their beds, she too, her duties done, passed through the silent hall on her way to rest, and as she went the child in her womb cried out. The cry roused all the guests, so that they sprang to their arms, all crowding together, none knowing the source or the cause of the cry which had roused them.

But Feilimi knew and told them, and Sencha, son of Ailill, bade him bring the woman before them that they might learn the significance of the cry. Feilimi brought her to them and said to her:

25

"That cry is a cry of terror and doom. Tell us, if you can, its meaning."

But she, bewildered and distraught with great pain and weariness, could tell them nothing. Instead she turned to the druid Cathbhad, a man of prophecy and deep knowledge, and mutely begged his help in her distress. He gazed on her with compassion, and turned to King Conor and the warriors, and spoke:

"The child who is soon to be born of Feilimi's wife will grow to be a woman of matchless beauty and form, of fair curling hair and steady clear blue eyes, of glowing cheeks and skin like new-fallen snow, teeth like pearls and coral-red lips. She will be the doom of kings and heroes and warriors. For her sake a host of good brave men will leave Ulster and go westward into exile."

Then the druid laid his hand upon the woman and again the child cried out, and the druid spoke again:

"'Tis a woman-child indeed that cries. She shall be called Deirdre. She will bring sorrow."

In a few days the child was born, and Cathbhad prophesied again her sorrow and her endless fame. At his words the young warriors clamoured for her death. But the king said:

"No. Tomorrow she shall be brought to me, and I shall have her reared apart from men, and in time she will be my wife and a companion to me."

The warriors murmured at this decision, but no one dared to speak against it. So the child was brought to Conor. He appointed for her foster-parents, and a woman-poet, Leorham, to be in charge of her until she grew to womanhood. He had built for them a house in a lonely place away from men, and no one had permission to approach or enter the house save these three who cared for Deirdre.

As Deirdre grew, her radiant beauty outshone even the words of the druid, and Leorham, watching over her with loving, tender care, dreaded the day when they would be parted. When the king would inquire if Deirdre was yet ready to come to him, Leorham would find an excuse for further delay. Thus Deirdre was in the fullness of her young womanhood, and thinking often of what manner of man she would marry if she had her choice, when one winter day of snow it happened that her foster-father killed a calf outside the house and the snow was reddened with blood and a raven flew down to drink it.

Deirdre, gazing on the scene, cried out:

"See, Leorham, the three colours. They belong to the man to whom I shall give my love. To him and none other. His hair black as the raven's wing, his cheeks red as the blood, his body white as the snow."

Leorham was sad when she heard the words. For she recognised part of the prophecy which the druid had made after Deirdre was born. Yet she wished the maid good fortune and told her that the man she spoke of was at Emain Macha, one of the bravest of Conor's warriors, one of the three sons of Usna. His name was Naoise.

"I shall never know comfort or content," said Deirdre, "until I see him and give him my love."

Not long after this Deirdre eluded her guardians and went to Emain Macha. By insistent questioning she had learned much from Leorham of the three sons of Usna: Naoise, Ardan and Ainnle; of their valour which was such that if they stood back to back the men of Ulster could not have overcome them; of their swiftness of foot, which was such that they could outrun their quarry in the hunt; of the music of their voices which was such that all were enraptured by it and even the cows on hearing it gave two-thirds more than usual of milk; of their loyal love for one another, which was such that each would give his life for the others.

Now, as it happened, when she came to Emain Macha, Naoise was standing alone on the rampart, and as she approached, he began to sing his melodious war cry, and the air was rich with it as she ran past where he could see her. His song was stilled by the wonder of her beauty, and as he quickly thought who she might be, it came to him that she could be none other than Deirdre of the prophecy, else such beauty could not have been hidden from the men of Ulster until now.

Deirdre gazed blushingly shy yet bold upon him, and he felt the love of her heart come to him and was troubled. For he knew she was betrothed to the king. Meanwhile his brothers hearing his song begin and then cease suddenly had run to him, and had heard Deirdre say that she loved him and could love no other. They warned him of the wrath of Conor, but the intensity of her love had won Naoise's love in the moment that he felt her love come to him. He took her in his arms and said: "Since we cannot stay here, we must flee. Come."

And Ardan and Ainnle went with them. First they travelled through Ireland, the three giving service of their arms to one king after another, pursued always by the wrath and wiles of Conor. Finally they were compelled to leave the country and voyage to Scotland, where they lived in wild places, hunting and raiding, until the king of Scotland took them into his service: for he had need of such valiant defenders.

They built houses for themselves apart on the green before the king of Scotland's stronghold, and the reason for this was that they were afraid that men might see Deirdre, and that blood might be shed on account of her beauty. But one day the king's steward, being out very early in the morning, chanced to look into Naoise's house, and there saw Deirdre and Naoise asleep. Immediately he rushed to the king.

"Until now," he said, "we have been unable to find a woman fit to be your wife. This morning I have seen a woman worthy to be wife to the emperor of the western world."

He told the king then of the ravishing beauty of Deirdre as she lay sleeping by the side of Naoise, and urged the king to have Naoise slain and Deirdre brought to him to be his wife.

"No," said the king; "but let you go to her house every day and woo her for me in secret."

So the steward came each day to Deirdre while Naoise was away, and each evening when Naoise returned she recounted to him all that was said and done. And the king became very impatient, for his courtship made no headway. So he began to send the sons of Usna into every extreme of peril, and even to invent dangerous missions for them, in the hope that they might be slain. But they returned from every mission victorious.

As time went on, the warriors of the king became aware of the king's plan and they sought every means they could to destroy the three brothers; and the strain of living under such hazardous conditions became so great that Deirdre pleaded with Naoise to flee from the place. And the sons of Usna fled by night and went to live on a wild, rocky island, safe from enemies but with little comfort or pleasure except in each other's company.

Meanwhile, news of their plight had come to Ireland, to the court of Conor, and the men of Ulster were indignant that the three valiant sons of Usna should suffer so much for the sake of

a woman. They begged the king to invite them back to Ulster, under his own protection.

Conor could not but accede to their request, though he had not forgotten the loss of Deirdre, and had not forgiven the sons of Usna. He said, therefore, to the men of Ulster:

"The sons of Usna will not return unless they have the word of a champion for their safety. And there are but three whose word they will accept: Conall Cearnach, Cuchulainn, and Fergus Mac Roi. I shall consult with these three and arrange for the safe conduct of the exiles."

He sent first for Conall and said:

"I intend no harm to the sons of Usna. Nevertheless, answer me this question. If I should send you to conduct them home, and if it should happen that they were to die through me, what would you do?"

Conall answered: "I do not wish to go for them, but if I did, and any harm came to them from any man, that man would not have long to live."

The reply did not please Conor, and he dismissed Conall and sent for Cuchulainn. But Cuchulainn made the same reply to his question, and he dismissed him also. He then sent for Fergus and put the same question to him, and his reply was:

"Conor, no harm can come to you from me, but after you there is no man would harm the sons of Usna and would not meet his death at my hands."

This reply pleased Conor, and he bade Fergus set out at once for the island that he might bring back with him Deirdre and the sons of Usna. And he gave him instructions to bring them ashore near the fortress of Borach at Dunseverick in the north, and he demanded the pledged word of Fergus that at whatever time of the day or night they landed they were to come straight to Conor at Emain Macha without stop.

Fergus gave his word and set out. When his boat touched at the island, Naoise and Deirdre were absorbed in a game of chess. It was Naoise's move, and Deirdre sat reflecting on a dream which the night before had disturbed her and which boded treachery and doom to those dear to her. Suddenly there was a loud cry from the beach: for Fergus was calling.

Deirdre knew the voice of Fergus, and knew in it the beginning of her dream's fulfilment.

Naoise looked up at her. "That was like an Irish call," he said. But she bade him make his move. "It was the call of some man of Scotland," she said.

The call was heard again. "I am sure that is the voice of an Irishman," said Naoise. But Deirdre again, in dread of the outcome, denied it.

As the call was heard a third time, coming nearer, Ardan and Ainnle ran up, and none of the three had any doubt but that it was the voice of Fergus. Naoise sent Ardan to meet him, and bring him to them.

It was a joyful and happy reunion when Fergus came and the men exchanged news and eager questions. Only Deirdre was sad, and she became even sadder as the three brothers became elated. She tried to dissuade them from accepting Conor's invitation to return to Ireland, but they only laughed at her fears and her forebodings, happy in the assurance of the word of Fergus that no harm would come to them from the men of Ulster. So they left the island, and Deirdre wept for the past and the future; for the happy days she had spent with Naoise and his brothers, for Scotland and its glens and islands which she had grown to love so much, and for the doom of her dream and her fate.

Meanwhile Conor had sent for Borach and had bidden him prepare a feast of welcome, for the exiles and Fergus, at his fortress in the north. For he knew that Fergus was under *geasa* not to refuse a feast which was prepared for him. And so Borach met the sons of Usna and Deirdre and Fergus when they landed, and invited them to his feast. Fergus was sorely grieved, for his word was pledged to Conor that the exiles should go straight to Emain Macha. Yet he could not break his *geasa*.

After much argument the brothers and Deirdre went on ahead, with the two sons of Fergus as their escort. Deirdre tried again to stem the tide of fate by pleading with them to go to Dundealgan to the fortress of Cuchulainn; but they deemed themselves safe in the protection of their own valour and the word of Illan Finn and Buinne, the sons of Fergus. And so they came to Emain Macha.

Out of her dreams and forebodings Deirdre spoke to them again: "There is treachery in this homecoming, and I have a sign by which you can know it. If Conor means no harm to you, he will invite you now to his house to meet his heroes and warriors; but if he intends your betrayal, he will arrange that you be received at the Red Branch."

When their coming was announced, Conor asked his steward if the Red Branch was prepared for guests, and being told that it was, bade him conduct the sons of Usna and Deirdre to it.

They were well received, and the finest foods and drinks were set before them and all in the party were gay with welcome except themselves. For the words of Deirdre had left them uneasy, and even though they had travelled far they ate but little. And Naoise called for a chessboard and sat down to play with Deirdre.

During all this time Conor was thinking of Deirdre, and at last he called Leorham to him and asked her to go and see Deirdre and tell him how she looked, and what change there was on her. For if she was changed he would let her stay with Naoise, but if not he would take her from him though blood should flow for it.

But Leorham loved her, and when she saw her great beauty, matured and refined and sad, she wept. And she told the sons of Usna that they were in the gravest danger, for if Conor learned that Deirdre had grown even more beautiful than when she left Ireland, he would let nothing stand in the way of his desire for her. So she bade them keep the house bolted and shut from outside gaze, lest someone see Deirdre and betray them. And Deirdre wept for her fate, that all her life since she was born she must be shut from the gaze of men lest the sight of her bring sorrow to those she loved.

When Leorham reported to Conor that all Deirdre's beauty was faded with the years, but that the sons of Usna were strong and valiant as ever and ready to serve him truly, he was pleased for a time and content. But the old desire gnawed within him, and after a while he called to him Trendorn, an enemy of Naoise, and bade him go see if Leorham had told him the truth. He went to the Red Branch, and in spite of all they had done within to keep out the gaze of prying eyes he found a place from which he could see Deirdre, and rushed back to Conor with the news of what he had seen.

Conor arose and called his men and set out to the Red Branch. But it was valiantly defended. First then, he persuaded Buinne the son of Fergus to accept a bribe to leave the sons of Usna; and Illan Finn, brother of Buinne, enraged at such treachery, made terrible slaughter of Conor's men, until he was killed.

The three brothers then took turns at watching and resting, and each time they sallied out they routed and slaughtered Conor's men. So Conor sent for his druid and told him that the men of Ulster would all be killed unless the sons of Usna were checked, and he bade him work an enchantment on them so that they would come out from the Red Branch unarmed. And Conor gave his word as a king and a warrior that no harm would come to them from him. The druid therefore obeyed him, and the sons of Usna came forth.

Conor then ordered them to be bound and brought to him, and asked who would kill them for him. But none of the men of Ulster would harm them. Again he called, and a man of Norway, Maine, came forward and offered to carry out Conor's command: for Naoise had killed his brothers. As he stepped forward Ardan cried out:

"If we must be killed, kill me first, that I may not see my brothers die."

Ainnle made the same plea. But Naoise said: "We shall all die together, if Maine will use the sword that was given me by Manannan Mac Lir. At one stroke it will kill all three." And thus the sons of Usna died, that Conor might have Deirdre.

When Fergus arrived and saw what had been done he burned and destroyed Emain Macha, and betook himself to Connacht, to the court of Maeve and Ailill at Cruachan. And that is the reason why Fergus was on the side of the Connacht queen when she planned the great cattle raid of Cooley.

And Emain Macha and Conor and all his line were cursed by the druid. And the fate of Deirdre was fulfilled. But she herself had died at the moment when the sword of Manannan Mac Lir struck the sons of Usna; and she lay with Naoise in death.

CHAPTER V

Bricriu

BRICRIU POISON-TONGUE arranged a great feast for King Conor Mac Nessa and all the men of Ulster; and he spent a whole year on the preparations for it. He erected a magnificent banqueting hall, on which was employed all the artistry of the greatest designers and decorators and jewellers and craftsmen of the time. And there were lofty windows of glass in either end of the hall, and above one of them was a balcony from which one could survey all that went on within.

When the building was completed and furnished, and stores of food and drink had been laid in for the feast, Bricriu went to Conor at the headquarters of the Red Branch at Emain Macha and announced his invitation to the king and the men of Ulster.

And the king said: "I am pleased to accept your invitation if the men of Ulster are pleased."

And Fergus Mac Roi, for the men of Ulster, said: "We cannot accept the invitation. For if we go to the feast the number of our dead will greatly exceed the number of our living, when Bricriu's poison tongue has sown dissension and set us against each other."

"You had better come," said Bricriu meaningly.

"Explain yourself," said Conor.

"If you come not," said Bricriu, "I shall stir up strife between kings, leaders and fighting men until they have slain one another, every man of them."

"We shall not permit you," said Conor.

"Then I shall stir up hatred between father and son; and, failing that, between mother and daughter, aye and amongst all the women of Ulster so that they come to deadly blows, and the very milk in their breasts become loathsome and rotten."

And Fergus said: "It may be better to go."

And Sencha, the wise, said: "Let us all consider this matter seriously."

And Conor said: "We must take counsel against Bricriu or he will do us harm."

And Sencha advised that they should accept the invitation on condition that Bricriu should not be at the feast himself but should retire as soon as the tables were laid, and that he should give hostages for the fulfilment of this condition. And the men of Ulster agreed to this, for they liked the idea of a feast, and Bricriu agreed and gave hostages, and eight swordsmen were selected to compel his retirement from the feast. And all the great host set out for the feast, and the ladies of the court went with them.

Now Bricriu's purpose in arranging the feast was to cause trouble in Ulster and to set the heroes of Ulster fighting with one another; and he set himself to the achievement of his purpose at once. He went first to Laoghaire the Triumphant.

"Laoghaire," he said, "mighty mallet of Bregia, hot hammer of Meath, red thunderbolt warrior of Ulster, what is there to prevent you having the title of champion of Emain?"

"It is mine if I choose to claim it," said Laoghaire.

"Chief of the champions of Ireland you can be," said Bricriu, "if you do as I advise."

"I will do it," said Laoghaire.

"All you have to do is this," said Bricriu. "When the portions are being served at the feast, let your charioteer rise up and take to you the champion's portion."

And Bricriu told him that the champion's portion at his feast

36

was no silly token but a prize worth contending for: a cauldron in which three men could stand, and the full of it of fine wine; a seven-year-old boar whose lips nothing had entered since it was young but fresh milk and fine meal in spring, curds and sweet milk in summer, nut kernels and wheat in autumn, and meat and soup in winter; a seven-year-old bull whose lips nothing had entered since it was a calf but sweet milk and herbs, meadow hay and corn; and five score cakes of wheat cooked in honey, and a quarter of a bushel of wheat had gone into each cake.

"There shall be dead men around me if I do not receive it," said Laoghaire.

And Bricriu smiled, and betook himself to Conall Cearnach and was even more successful with him in his plan of dissension.

Then he went to Cuchulainn, and when he had made his speech about the virtues of Cuchulainn and his right to the champion's portion, Cuchulainn cried: "By the gods of my people, whoever tries to claim the champion's portion before me shall lose his head."

And Bricriu went away well satisfied.

By this time there was music and merriment in the hall, and when the tables were laid Bricriu was expelled and went on to his balcony with his wife and followers; but before he left he announced the champion's portion and instructed that it be given to the hero whom the men of Ulster preferred for valour. And immediately the three charioteers stood up, and first, Sedlang Mac Riangabhra claimed it for Laoghaire, and the second, Id Mac Riangabhra, claimed it for Conall, and the third, Laeg Mac Riangabhra, said: "Bring the champion's portion to Cuchulainn. It is no disgrace for any Ulsterman to yield it to him; for he is the greatest hero of you all."

"That's a lie," said Laoghaire and Conall together.

And immediately they attacked and Cuchulainn defended, and the hall rang with terrible clangour of the heroes' arms, and the flash of sword and spear was like lightning and the rattle on shield and armour was like thunder, and the men were a glittering white haze behind the enamel of their shields.

But Conor and Fergus were enraged at the two men attacking one, and Sencha said to Conor: "Separate them." And Conor separated them.

And Sencha said: "Tonight the champion's portion will be divided. As to who is champion let Ailill decide at Cruachan."

And they were all satisfied with that, except Bricriu, who from his sun balcony viewed with disgust the warriors' return in peace to their feasting.

As he watched the festivities, however, and saw the excitement and hilarity mount, he cogitated his second plan. And as Fedelma, wife of Laoghaire, tripped forth from the palace gaily, surrounded by her fifty ladies, he addressed her and flattered her beauty and her lineage and her husband's valour. Then he suggested that if she were to enter the banqueting hall first she would be acclaimed first of all the women of Ulster. And he spoke likewise to Lendabair, wife of Conall, and to Emer, wife of Cuchulainn; and with Emer he excelled even himself in flattery and incitement to pride and arrogance.

And when it was time for them to enter the hall, the three groups moved off gracefully together, each group unaware of the others' intention. And over the first ridge on their way to the hall they went at even pace, elegant and graceful; over the second ridge their steps were short and quick, not so elegant; and over the third ridge they came with their long robes caught up in their hands and their knees in the air at full speed like athletes at one of the great festivals, a graceless, inelegant, screaming mob.

And the warriors within the hall sprang to arms as they heard the shouting and tumult. But Sencha, being wise and seeing Bricriu's hand in the tumult, bade the warriors close all the doors, so that there should be no cause within for dissension. And the doors were closed just as Emer, wife of Cuchulainn, reached the main door, panting, and turned with her back to it, to face the other women triumphantly.

But each of the three women called to her husband within to let her in, that she might enter first of all the women. And Bricriu smiled, for he knew the women would cause trouble. And Conor was troubled, and he struck the gong for all to be seated.

And Sencha said: "Let there be no battle of arms but a battle of words."

Thereupon each of the three wives sang a poem in praise of themselves, their birth, their beauty and their brave husbands. And Emer sang longest and haughtiest of the three.

And Laoghaire and Conall arose and broke an opening in the walls for their wives to enter; but Cuchulainn arose and heaved up the whole banqueting hall to the stars on one side. And when

Emer entered he brought it down again so forcibly that seven feet of the wall entered the earth.

And Bricriu and his wife and the balcony went down with it. And he was so bespattered with mire and dust that only by his voice raised in cursing and invective did they recognise him. Nor could anyone set his hall to rights again, that they might continue the feast, until Cuchulainn was prevailed upon out of his strength to set it upright. But the champion's portion was still unsettled. And Conor was unhappy; for strife and dissension were in the air while the matter was undecided. So he said to the three heroes: "Go to Curoi Mac Daire for a judgment; his judgment is true; but to ask him demands courage."

At the word, Laoghaire yoked his chariot and leaped upon it. He drove by gaps and fords and meadows, by the Fews of Armagh and the four road ends past Dundalk till he came to Bregia, where a thick druidic mist surrounded him. Here perforce he alighted, and told his gilla to put the horses in a meadow near by.

When the gilla was in the meadow a huge, muscular giant approached, ugly-wrinkled, bushy-eyebrowed, unkempt, tattered and down at heel, with a monstrous club over his shoulder.

"Whose horses are these?" he roared.

"The horses of Laoghaire the Triumphant," replied the gilla.

"Aha, a fine bucko that," said the giant; and brought the club down on the gilla with a blow that rocked him from head to heel. And the gilla yelped loud and long like a kicked cur.

"What are you doing to my gilla?" shouted Laoghaire.

"Making him pay for the damage to the meadow," said the giant.

"I'll settle that," said Laoghaire; and threw himself upon the giant. But the giant was too strong for him, and in the end he had to flee as best he could.

And when Conall came along a like fate befell him, and he too, like Laoghaire, left behind his gilla and his chariot and his arms when he fled.

But when Cuchulainn came he worsted the giant after a mighty struggle, and returned to Emain Macha with the horses, gillas and equipment of Laoghaire and Conall as well as his own.

But even this did not settle the allocation of the champion's portion; for Laoghaire and Conall maintained that the interference of magic and fairy folk had rendered the test invalid.

So they decided to abide by Sencha's original suggestion that they go to Cruachan, to Ailill and Maeve. And the earth shook as all the great host who went with them drew near to Cruachan: such was their clatter on it. And Maeve said: "Thunder in a clear sky."

And her daughter Findabar said: "Mother, I see a chariot coming across the plain."

"Describe it to me, and the hero in it," said Maeve.

And Findabar described the chariot and the hero.

And Maeve said:

> *"I recognise that man:*
> *peer of kings; contriver of victory;*
> *fury of fight; fire of judgment;*
> *flame of vengeance; mien of a hero;*
> *features of a champion; heart of a dragon.*

'Tis Laoghaire of the red hand and he will destroy us as he would cut leeks with a knife if we do not handle him tactfully."

And Findabar said: "Mother, I see a second chariot approaching."

"Describe it to me and the hero in it," said Maeve.

And Findabar described the chariot and the hero.

And Maeve said:

> *"I recognise that man:*
> *the roar of a lion; a wolf among cattle;*
> *head on head, and battle on battle he heaps.*

'Tis Conall Cearnach, and he will destroy us all as he would cut a trout on red sandstone if we do not guard against his rage."

And Findabar said: "Mother, I see a third chariot thundering towards us."

"Describe it to me and the hero in it," said Maeve.

And Findabar described the chariot and the hero.

And Maeve sighed: "I recognise him: 'tis Cuchulainn, and by the god of my people I say it, if Cuchulainn comes to us in fury he will grind us to mould and gravel as a mill of ten spokes grinds hard malt, unless we subdue his fury and assuage his violence."

And she gave orders for the entertainment of the host on a magnificent scale; so that there was feasting and merriment and pleasure of every kind for everyone for three days and nights.

Then Ailill asked Conor the purpose of the visit; and Sencha replied and told him. And Ailill was unhappy; for he feared the anger of the other two if he decided in favour of one.

"Give me three days and three nights to consider it," said Ailill. They agreed, and the great host departed, pleased with their entertainment, leaving the three heroes with Ailill and Maeve.

That night three magic cats were let loose upon them in their hall; and Laoghaire and Conall climbed to the rafters and left their food to the cats, but Cuchulainn remained and ate and drank his fill, and though he could not kill the cats, for they were magic, neither did they cause him to flee. In the morning, therefore, Ailill would have judged according to this test, but Laoghaire and Conall refused to accept such a judgment. "'Tis not against magic beasts we test our valour," they said, "but against men."

And Ailill was distraught, and he neither ate nor slept for the remainder of the time; and still he could not commit himself to a judgment. So Maeve took the matter in hand. "Coward," she said to Ailill, "if you do not decide I will."

So she called Laoghaire to her and gave him a bronze cup on the bottom of which was a bird chased in silver, as a token of her judgment that his claim to the champion's portion at the feast was valid. But she warned him not to show it until all were together at the Red Branch and it was time to allocate the champion's portion. And Laoghaire quaffed the full of the cup of fine wine and went his way satisfied.

And to Conall she gave a cup on the bottom of which was a bird chased in gold, with the same assurance and the same instructions; and he too quaffed his wine and went off satisfied.

Cuchulainn was not so easily satisfied, for he knew the insincerity of Maeve's blandishments; but in the end he accepted a cup of gold with a bird set in precious stones on it, and along with this the size of his two eyes of dragon stone.

"Now," said Maeve, "you have the feast of a champion, and may you enjoy it a hundred years at the head of the heroes of Ulster. And as you yourself are incomparable among the heroes of Ulster, so is your wife among the women of Ulster, and should always precede the other women when entering the banquet hall." And Cuchulainn also quaffed the full of his cup of wine. But before he departed he sought out the women of Cruachan and taking thrice fifty needles from them he tossed them in the air one after

41

another; and each needle went into the eye of the one before it, so that they were all joined together. And then, returning thanks for the pleasures of his stay, he gave each needle into the hand of its owner and departed.

But the question of the champion's portion was not settled yet; for Maeve's trickery was recognised; and although Cuchulainn's cup was the fairest and most costly, Laoghaire and Conall refused to allow the judgment to him; for they alleged that he had bought such a costly token with jewels and treasures.

And indeed there was no test that they tried, and they tried many, which gave a judgment on which all three would agree; until the night of the champions' covenant.

The men of Ulster were in Emain Macha and they were weary after a great festival and the games and contests. And Conor Mac Nessa was there and Fergus Mac Roi; but of the three great heroes only Laoghaire was present.

The sun was setting and in the dim light during a lull in the talk a huge figure was seen at the end of the hall. And they awaited his approach and noted the details of his ugliness and gracelessness as he drew nearer. He wore an old leather singlet and over it a dull brown cloak, and on his shoulder he carried as a club a great tree, under which thirty bullocks could shelter. In his right hand he carried an axe and its edge was so keen that even a hair blown against it by a puff of air was cut in two by it.

And he went over and stood by the fire and addressed himself to Conor and the men of Ulster.

"I am on a quest," he said. "Neither in Erin nor in Alba, in Europe nor Africa nor Asia have I found what I seek. I have been to the isles of Gades and the Pillars of Hercules, to Greece and to Scythia, and I have not found it, nor the man of honour I need for it. But you, the men of Ulster, they say, excel the men of all countries in vigour and virtue and valour, in dignity, in truth and in honour; and so among you I hope to find at last what I seek."

"Make known your quest, then," said Fergus Mac Roi.

"I will," said he, "if I can find a man to honour his word on it."

Said Sencha: "If you are to find such a man anywhere, you will find him here."

"Very well so," said the giant. "I want a man to make covenant with me and keep it. And it is this, that he should cut off my head tonight and I cut off his head tomorrow night."

And he paused, waiting; but no one spoke.

Then he added: "Will any of the warriors who claim the champion's portion make this covenant with me and keep it?"

And again there was silence; for no one could understand his speech. And there was a weariness about him as if he did not expect to find the man he was looking for. He spoke again: "Is Laoghaire the Triumphant here? Is he afraid to come forward?"

And Laoghaire stepped forward roaring: "The man who says I am afraid will pay for it with his head."

"Very well so," said the giant. "My head tonight."

And there was an angry swish as Laoghaire swung the axe, and the giant was down and his head rolling into a corner of the hall.

But as Laoghaire turned to go back to his seat a voice stopped him: "Your head tomorrow night. That is the covenant."

And to the horror of all the giant arose, picked up his head and his axe, and was gone. And there was no more talk that night.

On the next night the company was assembled in gloom; but Laoghaire was missing. And the giant, in a sad voice out of keeping with his terrifying appearance and the ghastly memory of the previous night, complained of the lack of honour even among the men of Ulster.

And Conall Cearnach, who was present, was constrained out of shame to maintain the honour of the Red Branch. And it befell him as it befell Laoghaire. And on the third night he too was missing.

But Cuchulainn was present. And the giant taunted him: "Men of Ulster, your vaunted valour is no more. Your warriors covet the champion's portion but they lack the honour and the fidelity to their covenant without which no man may lay claim to it. And what of that wretched little creature, Cuchulainn? I suppose his word is no better than that of the others, even if he had the courage to make the covenant."

"I need no covenant," roared Cuchulainn in a fury.

"Because you have not the courage to keep it," said the giant quietly.

With that Cuchulainn snatched the axe and swooped the head of the giant, clean cut from the neck, up to the highest rafter of the hall. And the giant caught it as it fell, and took the axe and went off.

And on the morrow there was great dejection on the men of Ulster, and especially on Cuchulainn, but he remained in the hall.

And when the giant came he said: "Where is Cuchulainn?"

"Here I am," answered Cuchulainn.

"You have little to say, and that not too loud," said the giant.

And Cuchulainn said no more, but went up to the block and stretched his neck across it; but the block was very big.

"Stretch out your neck," said the giant. "It is awkwardly placed."

"There is no need to prolong the torment," said Cuchulainn. "I gave you a quick cut."

"But your neck is too short," said the giant. "You must stretch it out to the end of the block."

Cuchulainn said no more, but by a mighty effort stretched his neck till it reached the end of the block. And the giant swung the axe and it rang off the rooftree as it went up, and the swish of it was like the wind shrieking in a night of tempest. And the men of Ulster shivered in dread of what was coming. And the axe came down, and the blunt side of it patted the neck of Cuchulainn gently as the giant spoke: "Arise, Cuchulainn, for none of the men of Ulster is to be compared to you for courage and heroism and honour. Yours from this time forth is the sovereignty over the warriors of Erin, and yours the champion's portion, and to your wife Emer belongs precedence over all the women of Erin in the banquet hall."

And with that he vanished. And thus were the heroes of Ulster tested for the champion's portion.

CHAPTER VI

Cuchulainn

BIRTH

CONOR MAC NESSA was king of the Ulstermen. One day his sister, Dechtire, who was given as wife to Sualtam, disappeared from Emain Macha, along with fifty maidens. Nor could any searching find them.

They were missing for three years when one day Conor and the men of Ulster saw a great flock of birds descend on the plain of Emain Macha and consume and destroy the grass and every green thing growing there. In a rage Conor rose and called his men and went to his chariot to go in pursuit of the birds; and with him went Fergus Mac Roi, and Amergin, and Conall Cearnach, and Laoghaire the Triumphant, and Blai the Hospitaller and Bricriu Poison-tongue.

The birds flew south over Sliabh Fuaid, in the direction of the Boyne, but fast as the warriors went in their chariots they lost the birds before night fell. And Conor bade them stop and look for a place wherein to spend the night.

Conall and Bricriu went forward to find a place. They found a small house.

"It is a poor place," said Bricriu.

"It will serve," said Conall; and the others agreed when Conall went back and told them of it. But Bricriu had heard a noise outside and had gone to investigate it. He came to a magnificent hall near by and went in. A godlike youth of noble appearance stood before him.

"Welcome, Bricriu," he said.

"A thousand welcomes, Bricriu," said the handsome woman who stood beside the youth.

"Why is the woman's welcome a thousand to your one?" asked Bricriu.

"It is her welcome which I give you," said Lu, for it was he. "Have you been searching for anyone who is missing from Emain Macha?"

"Dechtire and fifty maidens have been missing these three years," said Bricriu, "and no one has been able to find them."

"And do you not recognise Dechtire here with me?" asked Lu. "Her fifty maids are here with her also. And it was they brought you here tonight. For they went in the form of a flock of birds and consumed the green of Emain Macha that you might pursue them and come here. For it is time for them to return."

Dechtire gave Bricriu a cloak of purple with fringes of gold, and bade him return for Conor and his companions. Bricriu went back for the company, but on his way he thought to himself that Conor would give a great reward for the return of the fifty maidens and Dechtire, and he reported merely that he had found a beautiful hall where they could all be entertained and rest for the night. So they went to the hall; but the mistress of the hall had excused herself from meeting the company that night: for she was with child.

In the morning Lu had vanished, but Dechtire sat in the midst of the maidens with a baby son in her arms. And Bricriu told Conor that Dechtire and the fifty maidens who had disappeared with her were in the house. And all returned rejoicing to Emain Macha.

Conor said that his sister Finnchoem should rear the child. But immediately there was a dispute: Blai, the Hospitaller, claimed that he should rear the boy: for so he would never want for anything; Fergus claimed by his valour, his strength, his position as envoy of the king, his championship of the weak against the strong, his power to teach and instruct in the ways of warfare, that he should have the boy; Amergin claimed by his fame for wisdom and courage and his powers as a poet that he should have the boy; and Sencha, the wise, claimed that none could dispute the tutelage of the boy with him, save only the king: for he counselled the king, he arbitrated between the Ulstermen, he had the wise words of peace.

But in the end Sencha himself, in his wisdom, declared that none should press his claim until Morann had spoken. And Morann's judgment was that all should share in the training of the boy, for he was destined for greatness, and for the valiant defence of Ulster: his name was destined to be in the mouths of all men: he would win the love of many: he would avenge all wrongs. Morann's judgment was accepted, and Finnchoem and Amergin took him to Dun Breth in the plain of Muirtheimhne. And the name given him was Setanta.

BOYHOOD

The truth of Morann's prophecy became clear as the boy grew. All the feats and knowledge of boyhood he learned long before the normal age, and he was only about five years old when he decided that he would go to Emain Macha. For he had just heard of the Boy Corps at Conor's court, and how Conor would divide his day into three parts, so that in one part he would watch the boys of the corps at their games, especially hurling, in the second part would play chess, in the third part would feast and listen to music and lays of the bards.

"I will go," said Setanta, "and match myself against the boys of the corps in their games."

"It is too soon yet," said his mother. "You are not old enough in years, and you must have a champion to protect you and ensure your safety with the boys of the corps."

"I cannot wait," said the boy, "until my years are deemed enough for that. Let you but tell me in what direction is Emain, so that I may go now."

His mother knew him, and without further argument pointed the way to him, over Sliabh Fuaid northwards. He took his hurling stick of bronze and ball of silver, his toy spear and sports javelin, and he shortened the way for himself with them: for first he would hurl the ball, then he would throw the hurling stick after it and hit it far from him, then he would throw the javelin and the spear, and in a quick spurt would catch the stick and the ball and the javelin, and lastly the spear by its tip, before they touched the ground.

Thus he made his way to Emain Macha, where he found the boys of the corps, three fifties in number, playing at hurling and games of warfare, with Conor's son Folloman at their head. He ran in amongst them at the hurling and guiding the ball before him, drove it along so that it went no higher than his knee and no lower than his ankle, until he passed the goal with it. And none could stop him or take it from him.

Folloman looked in amazement at the little lad.

"He has no guarantee for his safety amongst us," he said. "He has interfered in our game. He is surely the son of some unknown. All this is to invite attack and revenge. We shall kill him."

They all attacked him with their hurling sticks, but he parried all their blows, and they could not harm him. The same with the balls from which he defended himself with hands and arms alone. The same with their toy spears which he caught on his toy shield. Then he turned to the attack and laid low one fifty of them. He was pursuing five of them past the place where Conor sat watching when Conor called:

"Stop, stop, boy. You are dealing very roughly with the boys of the corps."

"And I have good reason," said Setanta. "I came from a great distance to join in their games, and they attacked me. That is not a gentle way to treat a guest."

Conor explained that it was customary for a new-comer to the corps to obtain pledges of protection from the boys before entering amongst them. Setanta said he did not know of this: had he known he would have conformed to custom; for it would be easy for him to obtain pledges. He told Conor then who he was.

Conor called on the boys to give pledges of protection to Setanta.

"We grant it," the boys answered.

Setanta then returned to the play and in a short time a fifty of the boys were laid out on the green, so that their fathers thought they were dead. But in reality they had found the play so strenuous since the little lad joined them that they took refuge from it by lying down on the green.

"He is still playing too roughly," said Conor and called out: "Boy, what are you at?"

"They attacked me," replied Setanta, "until pledges for my protection were given by them. I will ease my attack when they ask pledges of me for their protection."

They all placed themselves at once under his protection.

THE HOUND OF CULANN

The following year the smith Culann invited Conor to a banquet, and asked him to bring only a few of his companions, as he had neither the space nor the means for a grand entertainment. Conor accepted, and, before he set out, he went as was his custom to see and say farewell to the boys of the corps.

He watched them at four games. In the first Setanta kept goal against all the three fifties, and they could not score; yet when they all kept goal together he scored against them as he wished. In the second Setanta guarded the hole, and though each of the hundred and fifty balls came to the edge of the hole, not one did he let in; yet when they all guarded together he had no difficulty in getting the ball past them into the hole. The third game was the tearing-off of mantles: Setanta tore all the hundred and fifty mantles off in a trice; they could not as much as touch his brooch. In the fourth game they wrestled, and with all the corps against him Setanta stood firm on his feet, yet when he turned to the attack he left not one standing.

Conor said to Fergus, who stood with him:

"If that lad's deeds when he is full-grown are in keeping with his deeds today, we are a lucky land to have him."

"Is there any reason to believe," said Fergus, "that his prowess, alone of all, will not increase with the years?"

But Conor said: "Let him come with us to Culann's feast. He is worthy."

"I cannot go just yet," said Setanta.

The king was surprised that the boy did not at once leave everything for the opportunity of going to a banquet with the select royal party.

"Why so?" he asked.

51

"Because the boys are not finished playing," said Setanta, "and I cannot leave until the games are finished."

"We cannot wait so long," said Conor.

"You need not wait. I shall follow you."

"You do not know the way."

"I shall follow the tracks of your chariots."

That was agreed. And Conor's party arrived at Culann's house, where they were welcomed to the feast which was ready laid for them. Culann said to Conor when the company were settling to the feast:

"Before we begin, tell me, is this all the company? There is none to follow?"

"None," said Conor: "all are here." He had already forgotten about Setanta.

"The reason I ask," said Culann, "is that I have a magnificent hound, which is my watchdog, and only myself can handle him or exact obedience from him; and none dare approach the neighbourhood when I loose him to guard the house. And I should like to loose him now before we begin."

"You may loose the hound," said Conor. The hound was loosed, and he made a circuit of the place and sat down with his head on his paws, a huge, fearsome guard.

Meanwhile the six-year-old boy had left his fellows of the boy-corps of Emain Macha, and was on his way to the house of Culann, the smith. He had no arms of defence, but passed the time of the journey with his hurling stick and ball. The hound bayed a fearsome challenge as he came to the house, but the boy continued his play until the hound sprang at him. Then he hurled the ball so that with terrific force it went right down the hound's throat, past the great open jaws and teeth, and as the hound reared back with the force of the blow and the pain, he grasped it by the hind legs and smashed its head to pulp on the stones of the yard.

At the sound of the hound's baying Conor had leaped to his feet remembering the boy. They all rushed out, certain Setanta was being torn by the hound, and were overjoyed to see him alive—all except Culann, who was filled with sorrow as he gazed on the hound.

"It was an unlucky day I made a banquet for Conor," he said. He turned to the boy. "You are welcome, boy, for your father's and mother's sake but not for your own. You have slain the only guard and protector of my house and my substance, of my flocks and my herds."

"Do not grieve," said the boy. "I shall see you are none the worse for what has happened."

"How can that be?" asked Culann, looking at the six-year-old boy.

"If there is a whelp of that dog's siring in all Ireland," said Setanta, "I shall rear and train it until it is able to guard and protect you as well as its sire; and until then I myself will guard your house and your property, even as your hound did."

"That is fair," said Conor.

"And you will be Cu Chulainn, the Hound of Culann, in the meantime," said Cathbhad the druid. "And that shall be your name, Cuchulainn."

"Indeed, I prefer my own name, Setanta, son of Sualtam," said the boy.

"But the name Cuchulainn will be on the lips of all the men of Ireland and the world, and their mouths will be full of its praise," said the druid.

"For that I would accept any name," said the boy; and from that time he was known as Cuchulainn.

THE TAKING OF ARMS

In the following year, when Cuchulainn was seven years in the world, he was playing one day some little distance to the south of the fort of Emain Macha. Now on the north side of the fort Cathbhad the druid was instructing his class of older pupils in druidic lore and learning. As was frequent with the youths, one of them asked the druid what was the fortune of the day, and whether he had anything special to say about it. The druid replied:

"He who first assumes arms this day shall be great and famous in arms above all the men of Ireland, and the stories of his deeds will be told for all time. Yet his life will be short."

Cuchulainn, even at the distance between them, overheard the words of the druid, and straightway dropped the playthings and rushed to Conor.

"All good be with you, O king," he called to Conor.

"And what do you seek for that fine salutation?" asked the king.

"I wish to assume arms," replied Cuchulainn.

"Who put that desire in your mind, lad?" asked the king.

"Cathbhad the druid," replied the boy.

"If it be on the word of Cathbhad you come," said the king, "your wish is granted." And he gave the boy two spears, a sword and a shield. For that was Conor's custom, to provide the members of the boy-corps with their arms, and to wish them good fortune with them.

Cuchulainn took the arms, and, testing them, shivered them into small pieces.

"These are not fit arms for me," he said. So Conor gave him another set. These too he smashed; and so with every set of all those Conor had ready for presentation to the young warriors. And Conor, though knowing Cuchulainn, was yet amazed at his strength and skill, and in the end took his own royal weapons and gave them to him. These Cuchulainn tested in every way he knew, and they stood the test.

"These are worthy arms, and fortunate is the land whose king has such," said Cuchulainn.

At that moment Cathbhad came into Conor's house and, seeing what was happening, asked in surprise:

"Is this boy taking arms?"

"On your word he is," replied the king.

"On my word?" asked the druid. "I did not suggest it."

"What did you mean, boy, by what you said to me?" demanded the king.

"His word it was that prompted me," said Cuchulainn, "when he told his pupils that he who should assume arms first this day would be famous, even though his life would be short."

"'Tis true. I said it," admitted the druid. "A name of glory and a short life."

"Were my life but one day and one night," said Cuchulainn, "it would please me, if only my name and the fame of my deeds live on."

"Be it so. In you will the truth of my word be seen," said the druid.

Cuchulainn called for a chariot. Again it was as with the arms. In testing he smashed every chariot that was brought to him, until Conor called to Iubar, son of Riangabhra:

"Bring my horses and chariot, and prepare them for this boy."

Cuchulainn tested the chariot and found it good.

"Now that you are satisfied, boy," said the charioteer, "let us turn the horses out to grass."

"Let us take a turn round Emain Macha," said Cuchulainn, "that I may receive the salutation of the boys of the corps." They did that, and the boys saluted him; but showed also that they would miss him at the games. But Cuchulainn told them that this was a special day, on which he must assume arms; but that he would return to them.

"Where does this great road lead to?" he asked the charioteer.

"To Ath na Foraire," he replied.

"And why is it called Ath na Foraire, the Ford of the Lookout?" asked Cuchulainn.

"Because a strong warrior of Ulster is on the lookout there every day, to see that no outsider come to do injury to the men of Ulster. For one day he is the champion of the whole of Ulster. And should any poet be leaving the province dissatisfied, the champion is to provide him with wealth and kind to comfort him; and should any poet be coming to the province, the champion is to escort him safe to Conor, and for that service the champion is the subject of the first verses of praise made by that poet when he comes to the house of Conor."

"And who is on the lookout today?" asked Cuchulainn.

"Conall Cearnach," replied Iubar.

"We will go to Ath na Foraire," said Cuchulainn. And in spite of Iubar's arguments and appeals they went to the ford. Conall welcomed the boy and wished him victory and first-wounding with his new-taken arms, though he thought it too soon for the boy to have taken them. Said Cuchulainn to Conall:

"Let you return now to Emain Macha, and I shall stay on the lookout."

"If it were merely to escort a poet, I might permit it," said Conall, "but I could not leave you alone to do battle with a warrior."

"Then I will go farther south," said Cuchulainn, "and perhaps on the border I may be first to meet a warrior, and blood my arms this day."

"Then I will come with you," said Conall; "for if anything were to happen to you there, the men of Ulster would hold me to account."

Cuchulainn was very angry that Conall should follow him, for if they chanced on an enemy warrior he knew that Conall would not permit him to fight alone. So he took a stone and slung it with all his strength at Conall's chariot and broke the shaft, and Conall tumbled on his face from the broken chariot.

"Why did you do that, you brat?" shouted Conall angrily.

"To see if my aim was true, and to ensure that I would have the chance of seeing alone whether I am fit to be a warrior in arms," replied the boy.

"A curse on your aim, and on you too," retorted Conall in a rage. "Not an inch farther will I go to protect you, even though you go to your own mischief."

Cuchulainn drove on: but though they waited long at Fertas Locha Echtran no one came with whom he could test his valour. And all the while Iubar complained of their stay away from Emain Macha and its entertainment of the evening. Yet when they did move, it was not homeward that the boy bade him go, but to Sliabh Morne, from the summit of which, at the White Cairn, he bade Iubar point out for him the landmarks of the country around, that he might know them on his future travels. Iubar showed him the plain of Breg, and Tara and Tailtiu, and Cletech and Cnobga, and Bru of the Boyne the abode of Angus, and the fort of the three sons of Nechta the fierce, namely, Foill and Fandall and Tuachall, whose boast, Iubar said, was that there were more Ulstermen dead at their hands than there were alive.

"To that fort we will go," said Cuchulainn. They went, and the boy slew the three sons of Nechta, and cut off their heads as trophies of his first day in arms. Other trophies he gathered on the way home: two magnificent stags which he outran and tied to the chariot to run behind, and twenty-four wild swans which he brought down alive with two sling-shots and attached also to the chariot, flying.

The return of the chariot to Emain Macha presented a terrifying appearance to Leorham, who was watching, and who saw also that the terrible fury of battle was on Cuchulainn and that the hero-light was playing around his head; so that it would go ill with any who came in his way.

"The heat of his fury must be cooled," said Conor, "or it will be a bad day for the youths of Emain."

They consulted and agreed on a plan. As Cuchulainn came

thundering forward in his chariot the women of Emain Macha bared their bodies and went to meet him, knowing his extraordinary modesty. When he came to them he bowed his head over the chariot that he might not see them; and suffered himself to be lifted from the chariot and placed in a vat of cold water. The heat of his fury was such, however, that the vat burst. When he was plunged into a second vat the heat was still so great that the water bubbled and boiled. But in the third vat he was cooled.

They put on him then his festive raiment, and the lad of seven years who had so gloriously assumed arms that day took his wonted place at the banquet, at the knees of the king.

THE WOOING OF EMER, AND TRAINING IN ARMS

As Cuchulainn grew he excelled all the men of Ulster at the many feats which were performed by the warriors of Conor. And the women of Ulster loved him for his excellence at the feats, for his beauty, for his wisdom and for the sweetness of his speech. And he had many gifts besides: prudence, until the terrible fury of battle came upon him, as it had come on the day he assumed arms; the gift of chess-playing; the gift of reckoning; the gift of prophecy. But he had three defects: he was too young, and his beardless face evoked the mockery of strangers; he was too daring; and he was too beautiful.

The men of Ulster were perturbed that the women loved him so much; and they deliberated about him, and resolved to look for a maiden who would be a suitable wife for him. They had in mind also the prophecy that he would die young, and they wished him to leave a son: for only from himself could his second birth come. So they sought long through Ireland for a suitable maiden for him to woo.

But Cuchulainn himself went to woo Emer, the daughter of Forgall the Sly. He went in his chariot, with Laeg, son of Riangabhra, his charioteer; and they found Emer seated on the level playing-field, teaching her companions fine needlework and crafts. Emer had all the gifts which Cuchulainn looked for in his wife. And so he had put on his fine festive raiment to come and woo her.

Hearing the noise of the horses and the chariot, Emer said: "Let someone look to see who comes."

"Two noble, spirited horses," said Fial, her sister, "a black and a grey, drawing a chariot of fine wood, with silver-bronze wheels, and a pole of silver mounted with silver-bronze, and a yoke of gold. In the chariot is a dark, melancholy man, fairest of all the men of Ireland. A beautiful deep-crimson cloak around him, caught at his breast with a brooch of inlaid gold. Two blue-white, blood-red cheeks. A ray of love in his look. With him a charioteer."

Cuchulainn bounded from his chariot and greeted Emer, who returned the greeting graciously and inquired whence he came. In his answer to this, and the questions which followed from her, Cuchulainn spoke in riddles and word-play, so that only she could understand. But he told her straight of his upbringing, and how it was shared, by the judgment of Morann, among the men of Ulster and Finnchoem:

"So I am beloved of them all, and fight for the honour of all equally. And I was begotten honourably of Lu, when Dechtire was at Bru of the Boyne. But what of you, O maiden, in what manner were you brought up?"

"In the old virtues," she replied: "in good behaviour, in chastity, in queenly station, in beauty."

"Good virtues," said Cuchulainn. "Why should we not become one? For this is the first time I have met a maiden who could converse with me as you have conversed, wisely and graciously."

"A question," said Emer. "Have you a wife already?"

"No," said Cuchulainn.

"But I am younger than my sister Fial here," said Emer. "And I may not marry before her. And she excels in all fine crafts."

"It is not with her I have fallen in love," said Cuchulainn.

Then they spoke in riddles again, and in riddles Emer told him that her suitor must slay a hundred on every ford from Scene Menn to Bannchuing Arcait; perform the feat of leaping the hero-salmon leap and slaying three times nine men, and with each blow sparing one man out of the nine; avoid sleep from Samhain to Candlemas, from Candlemas to Mayday, and from Mayday to Samhain.

"All that shall be done," said Cuchulainn.

"And the offer is then accepted," said Emer.

When Laeg and Cuchulainn were returning to Emain Macha,

the charioteer asked the meaning of his words to Emer and hers to him.

"Did you not understand that I am wooing Emer, and that I disguised my meaning so that the girls with her should not know my purpose. For if through them Forgall should learn of it he would try to prevent it."

But the girls told their parents of the conversation, and the parents told Forgall, and though he did not understand the words of the conversation he recognised the description of Cuchulainn and guessed his intention. He immediately made plans to prevent the match.

He went to Emain Macha disguised as a foreigner, claiming to be an ambassador from the king of the strangers, with gifts of gold and wine and treasures for Conor. A part of the entertainment given him was a display of warriors' feats, and he said that the warriors were excellent indeed, but that if Cuchulainn went to Donall the Destroyer in Scotland his skill would improve, and that if he placed himself under the instruction of Scahach the warrioress, who was in the east of Scotland, he would surpass all the warriors of Europe. His purpose was to have Cuchulainn involved in the battles and wars of Scahach and so lose his life.

So Conor, Conall Cearnach, Laoghaire the Triumphant and Cuchulainn decided to go to Scotland. But first Cuchulainn paid a secret visit to Emer, and she told him of Forgall's plot to separate them. And she urged him ever to be on his guard against the sly tricks of her father. The two promised to be faithful to each other, until they met again or the death of either. Then Cuchulainn went off with the other three to Scotland.

Donall the Destroyer taught them some feats, but said that Cuchulainn must go to the warrior woman Scahach to complete his learning. So they set out for the east of Scotland; but a vision of Emain Macha rose up before the others, some say by the power of Forgall, so that longing for home prevented them from going forward.

Cuchulainn went on alone, and wandered from the direct way. Suddenly in his path there appeared a great beast, like a lion. It came towards him. It stalked his movements. It offered him no hurt. Whichever way he went it went in front of him, turning its side to him. At last he accepted the implied invitation and leaped on its back.

Without guidance it went forward for four days, until they came to an island in a loch. Some boys were rowing a boat in the loch. They burst out laughing at the sight of a wild, untamable beast in the service of man. Cuchulainn jumped from the beast's back, and bade it farewell. Thus they parted.

Cuchulainn went forward, and on his way met a youth who told him that the road to the fortress of Scahach lay across the Plain of Bad Luck; that on the nearer half his feet would stick fast, and on the farther half the blades of the grass would rise and hold them. But the youth gave him a wheel and an apple and told him to follow the track of the wheel across the first half and then to hurl the apple from him forward and follow the way it travelled across the second half of the plain. When he had crossed the plain, the youth went on, he would have to go through the Glen of Danger, which was full of monsters raised up by Forgall to destroy him, and after that he would go over wild, fearsome mountains.

But with the youth's guidance Cuchulainn came past all the difficulties and dangers to the encampment where the pupils of Scahach were assembled. He asked where was Scahach.

"On the island there," they replied.

"How may I get to it?" he asked.

"Across the Bridge of the Pupils," said they. "But only a proved champion may find his way across it."

The bridge was arched, the two ends low and the middle of it high, and when anyone leaped on to one end of it the other end would rise up and throw him over backwards. Cuchulainn, not knowing this, jumped on to the bridge and was immediately tossed back on to the ground among the pupils, who roared with laughter at him. Again he tried, but with no more success; and a third time with greater effort he tried, but was again thrown back amid the jeers of Scahach's pupils.

The fourth time, with the fury coming on him, Cuchulainn made a quick jump on to the end of the bridge, performed his hero-salmon leap to the middle of the bridge, and reached the other end before it could rise sufficiently to toss him, and landed on the island safely. He went straight to the fort and with the shaft of his spear knocked on the door so hard that the shaft went through it.

Scahach sent her daughter Uachach to see who was seeking

entrance; and Uachach conversed for some time with Cuchulainn before she instructed him how he could compel Scahach to take him as a pupil. From Scahach he learned all the feats that were necessary to complete his knowledge of fighting, and he learned also, what no one else had learned, the use of the terrible spear, the Gae Bolg. And while he was a pupil there, Cuchulainn and Ferdiad, son of Daman, were united in the bonds of closest friendship and affection.

At this time Scahach was at war with the people whom the woman warrior Aoife ruled, and a great battle was about to take place. But Scahach was afraid that if Cuchulainn went into the battle some hurt would befall him. So she gave him a sleeping drug, which would have kept anyone else asleep for twenty-four hours, and went off to battle. After one hour, however, Cuchulainn was fully awake again, and followed her to the battle. The three sons of Aoife had come to do battle for her, while only Scahach's two sons were fit to go against them; and Scahach was deeply distressed; but Cuchulainn ran up and joined her two sons, and himself leaped on the three champions of Aoife and slew them.

Aoife herself then issued a challenge, and again Cuchulainn sprang forward. As he went he asked Scahach what it was that Aoife loved most.

"Three things," replied Scahach: "her horses, her chariot and her charioteer."

Cuchulainn and Aoife joined battle. Aoife smashed Cuchulainn's sword off at the hilt. Cuchulainn shouted: "Alas! Aoife's horses, chariot and charioteer have fallen down the cliff!" She looked round. Cuchulainn sprang upon her, seized her, threw her to the ground, grasped a sword and held it over her.

"My life, Cuchulainn," she begged.

"On conditions," he answered.

"Granted," she cried.

"That you give hostages to Scahach, and never again make war on her, and that you bear me a son."

And Cuchulainn left a ring with her, and told her that his son was to be named Connla, that he was to go to Ireland when the ring fitted him, when he would be seven years old, that he should not tell any man who he was, that he should not turn back on his way for any man, and that he should not refuse combat with any man.

Meanwhile Emer, though Forgall had tried by every means he could to force her marriage with another, waited for Cuchulainn in the fortress of Forgall. When Cuchulainn returned with the other Irish pupils of Scahach, he rested a while at Emain Macha and then set out for Forgall's dun. There he performed the hero-salmon leap across the three earthworks and struck at three groups of nine who opposed him so that eight fell of each nine, and the three brothers of Emer were spared. Forgall himself was killed in attempting to escape over the earthworks; and Cuchulainn carried off Emer and her foster-sister with their weight in gold and silver.

The warriors of the dun pursued them, and at every ford from Scene Menn to Bannchuing Arcait Cuchulainn slew a hundred men. Thus he had accomplished all the deeds which Emer had demanded.

At Emain Macha they were welcomed, and Cuchulainn took Emer as his wife.

THE DEATH OF CONNLA

The men of Ulster were encamped near the Strand of Eise when they saw on the waves of the sea a boat and in it a lad performing feats. He had a pile of stones in the boat, and he would put a stone in his sling and bring down a sea-bird, stunned but alive, Then he would revive the bird and let it go again. He performed also many feats of heroes such as those taught by Scahach.

Conor was perturbed when he saw the skill and power of the lad. He said: "Woe to us if grown men come against us from the land where that lad comes from. That lad must not land here. Let someone go to meet him and turn him."

First went Condere, for he was a man of eloquence and argument. The boy had reached the strand when Condere went down.

"You have come far enough, boy, to let us know who you are and whence you come, before you enter our country."

"I tell my name and origin to no man," said the boy.

"You may not land until you tell," said Condere.

"You may have the strength of a hundred," said the boy, "but you cannot prevent my landing."

Condere returned to Conor and said: " 'Tis not a man of reasoning you should send to that lad, but a warrior."

So Conall Cearnach went. "You perform pretty feats, lad," said Conall, mockingly.

"A pretty feat for you," said the boy; and sent a stone in the air from his sling so that the thunder of its noise in passing sent Conall over on his back, and before he could rise the boy had his two arms bound fast with the strap of his shield. Conall shouted for someone else to meet the boy. But he made a mockery of all who were sent against him.

Cuchulainn stood with Emer's arms about his neck, watching the scene. When the others had failed to stop the boy he moved forward. Emer tried to stop him.

"Even if he were my own son," he said, "I would kill him to save the honour of the men of Ulster." And he went to the boy and mocked him as Conall had done. But the boy taunted him in return; and Cuchulainn in anger cried: "Tell me your name or you die."

For reply the boy made at him with his sword. They fought, and at sword-play they were equal.

"Let us see if you can wrestle as well," said Cuchulainn; and the boy, though he came but to Cuchulainn's belt in height, closed with him; and they wrestled into the sea. But neither could throw the other. And the fury came on Cuchulainn, and he sent the Gae Bolg at the boy.

"Alas!" he cried, mortally wounded, "that is one trick Scahach never taught to me, nor to anyone except only my father, Cuchulainn." Then Cuchulainn saw the ring on the boy's finger. He took him up in his arms and carried him to the men of Ulster, and said in sorrow:

> Heavy the burden
> I bring with me to Irish soil:
> the great weapons of my son in one hand,
> and in the other his spoils.
> Here is my son for you, men of Ulster.

And the boy said: "If I had been among you alive for five more years, I should have conquered the men of the world for you. But since I die, point out to me the great warriors of Ulster, so that I may take my leave of them."

He put his arms around the neck of one after another, and then around the neck of his father, and died. And there was great fear on the men of Ulster when they saw the grief of Cuchulainn. And for three days no one dared go near him.

THE DEATH OF FERDIAD

When Maeve and Ailill of Connacht made the great cattle raid on Ulster, seeking to bring away the Brown Bull of Cooley, and the weakness was on all the rest of the Ulstermen, Cuchulainn stood alone against the forces of Maeve. And all the great and noble warriors whom Maeve sent against him he slew one after another, until only Ferdiad was left to match him.

Now Ferdiad was Cuchulainn's dear friend, from the days when they were pupils together with Scahach in Scotland, and he would not fight with Cuchulainn. But Maeve, with the help of her druids and poets of satire and abuse, compelled him to come to her, and arranged a feast for him. And Findabar, daughter of Maeve, sat beside him at the feast, and with caresses and smiles, and with every art of woman, aided her mother's purpose to make him drunk and merry. When he was drunk, Maeve promised him great rewards, in equipment, in raiment, in hospitality, in riches, in land, in rights and privileges at Cruachan, Maeve's stronghold, for himself and his descendants, and lastly her daughter Findabar as his wife, if he would consent to fight with Cuchulainn.

Drunk though he was, he replied to all this: "These are great rewards indeed, but I decline them, for I cannot fight with the foster-brother whom I love, my equal in arms and battle, Cuchulainn."

Maeve then, with her wonted guile, spoke as if she had not heard Ferdiad:

"Cuchulainn's word about Ferdiad is true, then."

"What word?" asked Ferdiad.

"He said it would be no great deed if you were to fall at his hands," she replied.

"That was not a fair word," said Ferdiad. "Nor would I ever say it of him. But if he said it, then tomorrow let him try to prove it." And thus did Maeve prevail on Ferdiad to go against his dear friend Cuchulainn.

Now Fergus Mac Roi, who since the betrayal and killing of the sons of Usna by Conor had been with Maeve and Ailill at Cruachan, was greatly troubled at Ferdiad's decision, and went straight to Cuchulainn with the word of it.

"It is not to fight with me I would wish Ferdiad to come here," said Cuchulainn, "and that not through fear of him but on account of my love and affection for him. For almost I would prefer to fall at his hands than that he should fall at mine."

"For that very reason also," said Fergus, "I urge you to be on your guard. For Ferdiad is a greater warrior than any you have met in this cattle raid. He has a skin of horn about him, and no point or edge has ever been blooded on it in battle. He is the lion's fury, anger's outbursting, the foe-drowning ocean, fate's destroying blow."

Said Cuchulainn: "I swear the oath my people swear, that in every limb and joint he shall be as pliant as a rush in the bed of a river under my weapons, if he come to meet me. From Samhain till Candlemas I have been here at this ford, opposing and resisting four of the five great divisions of Ireland. And I have not left my place for a single night. In all that time I have not given ground before any, man or host. I do not think I will give ground before him."

Fergus departed, and Cuchulainn went off to Dun Dealgan to his wife Emer, and stayed with her that night. As for Ferdiad, he slept heavily in the first part of the night, but awoke early and restless. His charioteer tried to persuade him not to go to the ford of combat, but he said:

"I have given my word. Almost I would prefer that I should fall by Cuchulainn's hand than that he should fall by mine. But I tell you, if Cuchulainn fall by my hand, then there shall fall also by my hand Maeve of Connacht and a host of the men of Ireland, because they twisted my word from me when I was drunk and merry."

When they came to the ford of the combat it was yet too early, and Ferdiad lay down to sleep again. As for Cuchulainn, he had slept well, and when it was time he leaped into his chariot and set out for the ford. As he went the air around him thundered and rattled and shrieked as with the din of demons, so that as he came near the ford the charioteer of Ferdiad, in terror, awoke his master, who arose and donned his battle armour.

"Welcome your coming," he shouted to Cuchulainn.

"It were fitter for me to give the welcome," said Cuchulainn, "for it is you have come to my country."

"Why is it, O good Cuchulainn," said Ferdiad, "that you have come to do battle with me? For when we were together with Scahach, you were wont to attend upon me, to arm me, to lay my bed."

"True," answered Cuchulainn; "because of my youth and my lack of height and size, I did those services for you. But I am in no mood today for such. There is not a warrior in the whole world coming against Ulster who would not be treated by me as a foe to be defeated."

Yet Cuchulainn tried to dissuade Ferdiad from the fight, quoting the treachery of Maeve and the wiles of her daughter Findabar.

"It would be long," he said, "before you could become less in my regard than a woman who has been given to fifty warriors before you. When we were with Scahach none could separate us, not the finest woman born, but always we fought together and played together, inseparable.

> *We were bound in friendship once,*
> *we were comrades in the hosting;*
> *one the bed at night we shared*
> *when we lay in heavy slumber.*
> *Weary, hard, as one, we fought*
> *in many countries, far and foreign;*
> *as one we wandered through the woods*
> *when we were Scahach's favoured pupils."*

Said Ferdiad in sorrow:

> *Hound of Culann, man of feats,*
> *hard we learned the craft of battle.*
> *Treachery now has come between us.*
> *Choose the order of our fighting.*

Said Cuchulainn: "Yours is the choice for this day, for you came first to the ford." Ferdiad chose, from the feats they had learned together with Scahach.

All day they fought, grim and determined, well matched. But neither could overcome the other. And when night came, Ferdiad questioned: "A truce, Cuchulainn?"

"A truce," Cuchulainn agreed. They threw down their weapons and advanced each into the middle of the ford. They threw their arms about each other and kissed in memory of their friendship. As their horses grazed together and one fire served for the followers of both, they were attended by their charioteers. And of each herb and charm that was brought from the fairy mounds to Cuchulainn he sent a share to Ferdiad, that he might have the same care as himself. And of the food and drink that was sent to Ferdiad from the men of the four provinces which opposed Ulster, he sent a share to Cuchulainn, who had fewer supporters to provide for him. So they rested in weariness and peace with one another.

They fought again the second day as fiercely, and at night embraced and cared for one another. But the third day their fight was bitter, and they parted without word or sign of friendship. The fourth day saw the end, for, though in every feat and skill they were matched, only Cuchulainn had the feat of the Gae Bolg, and with this he killed his friend.

As Ferdiad fell in his death agony, Cuchulainn caught him in his arms, raised him up, and carried him with all his equipment to the Ulster side of the ford so that he might die there and not to the west with men of Connacht. He laid Ferdiad down, and as he gazed upon his dead comrade a cloud of weakness came upon him; so that when Laeg bade him rise to meet attack he said:

"What is there to rise for now that he has fallen by my hand?" Then he began his long lamenting for Ferdiad

> *All was pleasure, all was play,*
> *till Ferdiad came to the ford of fray.*
> *One our teaching,*
> *one our reward:*
> *from our gentle teacher*
> *the gentle word.*

> *All was pleasure, all was play,*
> *till Ferdiad came to the ford of fray.*
> *Our deeds the same,*
> *our skill in the field.*
> *Together from Scahach*
> *we received the shield.*

All was pleasure, all was play,
till Ferdiad came to the ford of fray.
Loved pillar of gold
at the ford I felled you.
In attack of heroes
none excelled you.

All was pleasure, all was play,
till Ferdiad came to the ford of fray.
It seemed his strength
could never fade:
yesterday towering,
today a shade.

THE DEATH OF CUCHULAINN

All the men and women of Ulster knew when the day of revenge had come for the red rout and slaughter Cuchulainn had caused among their foes. With the aid of every art of man and magic his enemies had contrived his doom: they had lured him to the final battle. All the efforts of Emer, all the efforts of his friends, to dissuade Cuchulainn from the fight were in vain; vain were all their pleadings, all their wiles, to detain him. With Laeg, his prince of charioteers, with the Grey of Macha, prince of steeds, and Black Sainglenn, his other horse, in the chariot, he went by the road of Midluachra around Sliabh Fuaid, the terrible thunder about him in the air and the hero's light about his head; in his mind the glorious memory of his victories and deeds from boyhood and all through the cattle raid of Cooley and after; and the fury of battle in his heart.

"He is coming," said Erc, son of Cairbre, as the thunder came to his ears.

So they made a square of their shields linked together, and at each corner Erc stationed two warriors to feign fighting, and a satire-poet with them. Erc bade the satirists in their turn to ask for Cuchulainn's spear, for the prophecy was that a prince would be killed by it, if it were given when asked.

Cuchulainn drove against them in three courses, and in each course left slaughter in his wake. Then he noticed a pair of warriors in combat, and a satire-poet with them asked him to intervene. With a blow of his fist he slew both of them.

70

"I request that spear," said the satirist.

"My need of that spear is greater than yours could be," said Cuchulainn.

"I will satirise you for your meanness, if you do not give it," said the poet.

"Never have I been satirised for meanness," said Cuchulainn. "Nor will I now." And he gave the spear. Lughai, son of Cu Roi Mac Daire, got the spear.

"What will fall to this spear?" he asked the sons of Calatin.

"A prince," they replied.

Lughai flung the spear at Cuchulainn. It killed the charioteer, Laeg. Cuchulainn drew out the spear, drove the chariot himself, and attacked again. And again, in the same way, he was compelled to give up his spear, to the second satire-poet. Erc, son of Cairbre, took it. With the same question, and the same answer from the sons of Calatin, he flung the spear. It hit the Grey of Macha. Cuchulainn snatched the spear and the wounded horse left the chariot.

A third time Cuchulainn attacked and lost his spear to a poet. This time again Lughai took the spear, and cast it at Cuchulainn.

Cuchulainn was wounded mortally, his entrails lying on the cushion of the chariot before him as he fell forward. Black Sainglenn bolted, leaving the chariot and his dying master on the plain alone.

"Let me go to the water that I may drink," Cuchulainn begged of them. And they from a distance, for they were afraid to come near him dying though he was, granted him his request, on condition that he came back to them.

"If I cannot come," he said, "I will bid you come for me."

Then he gathered his entrails into him and went down slowly to the water. He drank, and washed, and called his foes to come. He went to a pillar stone and put his belt around it and bound himself to it, so that he might die standing

Said Erc to Lughai: "That man slew my father and took his head. It were meet that his head should be taken in return."

But the Grey of Macha came galloping back, and while the hero's light still played around Cuchulainn's head it protected him. Three courses it galloped round him, and fifty were slain by its teeth and thirty by each of its hoofs.

Then the battle goddess Morrigu, and her sisters, came in the form of crows and sat on Cuchulainn's shoulder, and Lughai knew it was time and went forward. He arranged Cuchulainn's hair on his shoulders and cut off his head. And Cuchulainn's sword fell from his hand, and cut off the right hand of Lughai. In revenge for this they cut off Cuchulainn's right hand also, and left his body there.

Conall Cearnach and the men of Ulster, hurrying to the attack of their foes, met the Grey of Macha and it streaming with blood. Together Conall and the Grey sought Cuchulainn's body, and the Grey of Macha went and laid its head on Cuchulainn's breast. Tears of blood dropped from its eyes.

CHAPTER VII

Drunken Interlude

THE arrangement made between the followers of Milesius and the Tuatha De Dannan was that the Tuatha De Dannan should occupy Ireland under the surface and that the Milesians should occupy the surface of the country. So the Tuatha De Dannan went underground, into fairy hills and brus, and established communication with the fairies; but they left behind five of their number for each of the five fifths of Ireland to excite conflict and discord between the people of the conquering race. And the five they left in Ulster were: Brea, in the hills of Breg; Reg, in the slopes of Magh Itha; Tinnal, in the slopes of Sliabh Edlicon; Grici, in Cruachan Aigle; and Gulban, in Ben Gulban.

Once when Ulster was greatest, during the time of Conor, there were three who shared its rule, namely Conor; his foster-son, Cuchulainn; and Fintan, son of Niall. Between them and their followers the Tuatha De Dannan were eager to cause conflict.

Now Conor had prepared a great banquet for the annual feast

of Samhain, and the measure of the feast may be judged from the fact that there were ready for it a hundred casks of every kind of ale. To celebrate the feast, Conor invited Cuchulainn and Fintan. When Leorham, sent by Conor, went to Dun Dealgan she found that Cuchulainn was preparing a banquet for his own people and was unwilling to leave it. But Emer his wife prevailed on him, and he bade his charioteer, Laeg, make ready. Then leaping into his chariot, he was off by the most direct route to Emain Macha. Sencha, son of Ailill, bade him welcome:

"Ever welcome your coming, glorious head of the host of Ulster, bright jewel of the valour of the Gael, dear, conquering son of Dechtire."

"That is the welcome," said Cuchulainn, "of a man who is asking for something."

"You are right," said Sencha.

"Name your gift," said Cuchulainn.

"I will," answered Sencha, "if I have fit securities."

"Name your securities," said Cuchulainn; "but on condition that I get a gift in return."

On this condition Sencha named Conall Cearnach, Conall Anglonnach and Laoghaire the Triumphant. And Cuchulainn for his securities, named Cormac son of Conor, Mesdead son of Amergin and Eochai son of Celtchar.

Sencha then named his gift: "What I ask of you, Cuchulainn, is that you cede to Conor for a year the third of Ulster which is in your charge."

Said Cuchulainn:

"If Ulster be the better of his having it for a year I cede it. For he is the well of kingship that cannot be defiled, of the line of kings of Eire and Alba. If Ulster then be the better of his rule, let him have it, but if at the end of the year it be not the better, he must then return to the rule of his own third." Sencha agreed.

When Fintan arrived, he was met by the druid Cathbhad, who said:

"Welcome your coming, fair youth of fame, first champion of all Ulster, unbreakable bulwark against plunderers and pirates, border defender of the province of Ulster."

"That is the welcome," said Fintan, "of a man who is asking something."

"You are right," said Cathbhad.

"Name your gift," said Fintan.

"I will," answered Cathbhad, "if I have fit securities."

"Name your securities," said Fintan; "but on condition that I get a gift in return."

On this condition Cathbhad named Celtchar, Uma, and Ergi Echbel. And Fintan for his securities named the three torches of valour of Europe, the three sons of Usna: Naoise, Ainnle and Ardan.

Then they went into the house, and Cathbhad spoke:

"Conor is now king of all Ulster, if Fintan will cede him his third."

"That is so," said Sencha, "for Cuchulainn gave his third."

"And my return gift," said Cuchulainn, "is that Conor should come to a feast at my house. And I have my securities to that."

"Where are my securities?" shouted Fintan. "For that is my return gift and I demand it."

The securities of each advanced with their followers and fought savagely, and there were wounds and death on both sides, until Sencha son of Ailill arose and waved his wand of peace. They paused then from their fighting and listened to him as he spoke:

"The time for the feast of Conor's kingship is at the end of his year. Why should you fight now? Wait until the time comes and there may be a peaceful solution."

"We agree to wait," answered Cuchulainn for all, "provided that you seek not to separate us then if there be no peaceful solution."

Sencha agreed. And they remained for three days and three nights feasting with Conor. When the banquet was over they returned to their respective forts.

At the end of the year the province of Ulster was a fountain of desire and wealth and prosperity, under the rule of Conor, and there was not a residence in it, north, south, east and west, without a son in it, in the place of his father and his grandfather, in service with his lord. And Emer said to Cuchulainn:

"Conor is surely now high king of Ulster."

And Cuchulainn replied: "It is no sad thing if it be so."

"It is time, then," said Emer, "to prepare the feast for his kingship; for he is a king now for ever."

So the feast was prepared, with a hundred casks of every kind of ale to accompany it. The same preparations were made, of food and drink, by Fintan. And the preparations of both were finished on the same day, and both set out for Emain Macha at the same time. Cuchulainn arrived first, but he had barely unyoked his horses from his chariot when Fintan arrived. Cuchulainn went straight to Conor and invited him to his feast.

"Where are my securities?" shouted Fintan.

The sons of Usna advanced; and Cuchulainn's securities advanced to meet them, and again a furious, bloody battle began. Nor could Sencha come between them; for he had made his agreement with them. Neither could Conor do anything, except to leave them his royal hall as the scene of their fight. His son, Furbaide, left the hall with him.

Now Furbaide was a foster-son of Cuchulainn, and there was a great bond of affection between him and Cuchulainn. Conor, gazing on his son who was distressed by the fighting, recalled this and said: "My son, if you would, you could bring peace to the men of Ulster who are now fighting within."

The boy asked how that might be. His father answered:

"By weeping and showing your grief at the conflict in the presence of your foster-father. For he was never in any conflict or battle that his mind could not be diverted by concern for you."

The boy therefore went back into the hall and wept and grieved in the presence of his foster-father. At once Cuchulainn came to him and asked the cause of his distress.

"'Tis all this fighting and quarrelling when Ulster is so peaceful and prosperous, and all for one night's feasting."

"I have pledged my word," said Cuchulainn.

"I have sworn my oath," said Fintan.

"If I may make a suggestion," said Sencha, "to ease the boy's distress. The first half of the night to Fintan, the second half to Cuchulainn, so that neither need give way."

They agreed to that, and the men of Ulster, with Conor, went to the banquet prepared by Fintan, each noble with his lady, each king with his queen, each musician with his company. And they were entertained as if no more than nine had come. And food and ale as for a hundred were set before each nine of them. And there were music and lays and eulogies. And jewels and treasures were distributed amongst them.

Cuchulainn called his charioteer, Laeg, son of Riangabhra, to him and instructed him:

"Go out, Laeg, and observe the stars, and watch as you have often watched for me, and come and tell me when the hour of midnight is come."

Laeg watched as he was instructed. At midnight he came in and called: "It is the time now, O hound of the feats."

Cuchulainn informed Conor, who stood up. As the king arose the company fell silent. For the men of Ulster were under *geasa* not to speak before their king; and the king was under *geasa* not to speak before his druid. Cathbhad the druid therefore spoke first:

"What is it you would say, high king of the men of Ulster?"

"Cuchulainn thinks it is time for us to go to his banquet."

So they all arose, but by common agreement the women and youths stayed behind while the men mounted their chariots.

Now the men were already drunken and merry with ale, and when Cuchulainn bade Laeg to give ardour of speed to the horses, the rest followed his example, and the whole company tore away madly from Fintan's fort of Dun Da Ben, by Cathair Osrin, by Li Thuaga, by Dun Rigain, by Ollarbi's shore, by the plain of Macha, by Sliabh Fuaid, by the ford of the watchman, by Cuchulainn's Port Noth, by the plain of Muirtheimhne, by the lands of Snaithi, across the river Boyne, by the plain of Meath, by Claither Cell, by the Brosnas of Blama, across the river of O Cathbhad, into the great plain of Munster, into the lands of the Deise Beg, in the extreme south of Ireland, into the lands of Cu Roi Mac Daire. And their path through the length of the country was like a whirlwind.

At this point Conor called a halt to the cavalcade, and said: "Surely we have never before come this way from Dun Da Ben of Fintan to Dun Dealgan of Cuchulainn."

And Bricriu said: "It seems to me that we are not in the territory of the men of Ulster at all."

And the others agreed.

"Who will find for us where we are?" asked Conor.

"Who but Cuchulainn?" said Bricriu. "He has brought us here, and he has often boasted that there is not a part of the country in which he has not slaughtered a hundred."

Cuchulainn asked Laeg: "Do you know where we are?"

Laeg replied: "No, indeed."

"But I know," said Cuchulainn. "Yonder is Limerick. Here is

77

the land of the Deise Beg. Before us to the south is the host in Cliu Mail Mic Ugaine, in the land of Cu Roi son of Daire son of Dedad."

While they were talking thus, there was a terrific fall of snow, so heavy that it piled up to their shoulders, and the men of Ulster raised stone columns to support shelters for their horses. And those stones remain as a proof of the story.

When Cuchulainn told the men of Ulster where they were, Bricriu cried out: "Woe to the men of Ulster!"

"No need to cry woe," said Cuchulainn, "for I can guide you back without delay."

"We have never before," said Fergna, "heard a counsel of weakness from Cuchulainn."

"What would you have us do?" asked Conor.

"To stay," answered Celtchar, for the others, "a day and a night where we are, to show that we have no fear of anyone. To go now would be a sign of defeat."

"Very well, then," said Conor. "Tell us, Cuchulainn, where may we stay?"

"Here is Aonach Clochair," answered Cuchulainn. "It is empty now, for there is no aonach in winter. And Tara Luachra is on the slopes of Luachair. There are buildings in it."

"To Tara Luachra, then," said Sencha. And for Tara Luachra they set out with Cuchulainn to guide them.

Now if Tara Luachra ever was empty, it was not empty that night. For a son had been born to Ailill and Maeve of Connacht, and he was given in fosterage to Cu Roi Mac Daire; and Ailill and Maeve had come that night, with their company, to drink to the end of their son's first month in fosterage. Eochai Mac Luchta was there, too, with his company. And Cu Roi Mac Daire with all Clann Dedad.

With Maeve also were her two druids, Crom Deroil and Crom Darail, foster-sons of the great druid Cathbhad. These two were on the wall of Tara Luachra, watching and observing, and Crom Deroil asked:

"Do you see what I seem to see?"

"What is that?" asked Crom Darail.

"Swords of red war and the tramp of hosts over the side of Iarluachair from the east."

"You see but the giant oaks we passed yesterday."

"If they be but oaks, why the chariots beneath them?"

"Not chariots but the royal raths we passed yesterday."

"If they be but raths, why the shining shields in them?"

"Not shields, but the stone columns in the doors of the raths."

"If they be but columns, why the host of red-shafted spears above the host?"

"Not spears, but the horns and antlers of the stags and wild cattle of the country."

At this point the king of the world, Cu Roi Mac Daire, hearing the argument of the druids, came on the wall, and the sun rose.

"Clear to see now is the host," said Crom Deroil. "Cu Roi Mac Daire, you have wit and sense, and you have heard our dispute. What do you see over the side of Iarluachair?"

Cu Roi Mac Daire answered with a lay:

> *If they be cattle, or the breed of cattle*
> *They are not the herd of one cow.*
> *A quick-tempered man of bloody battle*
> *Is on the back of each cow.*
>
> *With every cow there goes a sword;*
> *On every left a shield;*
> *Above the cows, row upon row,*
> *Dread, dread standards I see.*

At his word, the first of the Ulstermen broke upon the plain before the walls. With the thunder of their chariots spears, shields and swords fell from the walls, and the thatch of the houses dropped in great flakes, and there were tremblings and chattering of teeth, and fits and faintings, and the druids fell in terror from the walls, one outside and one within.

The great host stopped, and dismounted from their chariots, and so heated were they with ale and exertion that the snow melted around them. Crom Deroil went into the house where Maeve and Ailill and Eochai Mac Luchta waited anxiously to hear the cause and the source of the thundering clamour, whether it was from the air above, or across the sea from the west, or from the east from Ireland itself.

"From the east, from Ireland itself," replied Crom Deroil to their questionings, "comes a barbarous host, and I know not if they be Irishmen or foreigners. But if they are Irish and not foreigners, they must surely be the men of Ulster."

"Go and obtain their description," said Maeve, "and Cu Roi Mac Daire will tell us who they are."

Crom Deroil returned with the descriptions:

"First I saw a great host and every man in it the equal of a king, and in front of it three more noble than the rest. Foremost of the three was a tall keen-eyed warrior, his beard fair and forked, his hair reddish-gold, his cloak purple-bordered and pinned on his shoulder by a brooch of wrought gold, his shield purple-brown and rimmed with shining gold, his sword gold-hilted, embossed. A strong warrior at his right hand, his countenance fairer than snow. At his left side, a small dark-browed man, of splendid appearance. Behind the three a tall fair warrior, juggling two swords over the head of the hero in the centre, tossing them in the air past the hero's head, but so that their edges did not touch even one hair of his head."

"It is not difficult to tell who they are," said Cu Roi. "The hero in the centre is Conor, king of the Ulstermen, descendant of the kings of Ireland and Scotland. The fair-skinned man on his right is Fintan, son of Niall Niamglonnach. The small, dark-browed man on his left is Cuchulainn, son of Sualtam. The man playing at battle feats over them is Ferchertni, son of Cairbre. He is a king-poet of the king-poets. When Conor goes into enemy country, Ferchertni goes behind to guard him. Whoever would wish to speak with Conor must first find a way past Ferchertni."

"Next," said Crom Deroil, "I saw three in warriors' raiment, two young, the third old, with a forked, purple beard. They moved as if no one saw them, and so swiftly and lightly that they did not move the dew on the grass."

"It is not difficult to tell who they are," said Cu Roi; "Delbaeth, son of Eithliu, Angus Og, son of the Dagda, and Cermat Honeymouth, three of the Tuatha De Danann, who have come, unseen by the host, to arouse battle and conflict."

As Crom Deroil described them in turn Cu Roi named them: Conall Cearnach, Laoghaire the Triumphant, Uma, Celtchar, Dubhthach, the fierce Beetle of Ulster; Trisgatal, who killed three nines of men by his fierce look alone; Roimid, Conor's fool who would banish sorrow and weariness by his comic antics; even the Dagda, great god of the Tuatha De Danann, whose amusement was to kill the nine who attended him on either side by touching them with the rough end of his terrible iron staff, and then to reanimate them by touching them with the smooth end. When Crom Deroil had described all he had seen at his first gaze he returned to the wall and called down to Cu Roi and Maeve and Ailill the descriptions of those who were now visible to him, and his last description was:

"Here I see a grave, grey-haired man, with a fair bright cloak about him, bordered with silver, a white mantle beneath, a silver belt about his waist. There is sweet melody in his clear, slow speech."

"That is Sencha, the great, son of Ailill," said Cu Roi, "most eloquent of all the men on earth, the peacemaker of the men of Ulster. He would bring peace to all the men of the world, from the rising to the setting sun, with his three fair words."

"All the host of the Ulster warriors is outside," said Maeve.

"None is missing," said Cu Roi.

"If their coming be in prophecy, there is a preparation for them in the prophecy also," said Maeve.

They went therefore to the eldest of the Clann Dedad, Gabal-glinne, son of Dedad, who was thirty years blind, and put their questions to him.

"Long has their coming been in prophecy, and there is preparation for them. A house with iron walls, with wooden walls covering the iron outside and in; a spacious cellar beneath, filled with every kind of inflammable material, and covered over with strong iron. The nobles of Ulster will gather into the house for the night, and seven strong chains will fasten the door to the seven stone pillars that are on the green outside."

Maeve spoke to Cu Roi: "Let an emissary from me and an emissary from you be sent to bid them welcome."

Cu Roi agreed, and said: "If the two be answered by Dubhthach the Beetle, then the Ulstermen mean war, if by Sencha, then peace."

They were answered indeed by Sencha: "Your welcome is pleasing to us and to our king. We come not in conflict or to inflict injury, but in a drunken ride from Dun Da Ben, and we think it not in keeping with our honour to leave this district without staying one night in it."

Cu Roi and Maeve then sent bards and poets to entertain the

Ulstermen while a meal was being prepared for them, and they also sent a message that the greatest hero of the Ulstermen should come and select the choicest house for them. A quarrel immediately arose among the heroes of Ulster as to who should select the house. But Sencha quelled it by his words:

"You set out in your chariots from Dun Da Ben to go to Cuchulainn's house, and you are under his security until you return. Therefore the house you occupy this night must be Cuchulainn's choice."

Cuchulainn then advanced, followed by the men of Ulster, and he chose the largest house in the place. And it was the house of the prophecy.

Food and ale were brought to them in plenty, and servants and attendants waited upon them, and they feasted and were entertained by song and lay, and they relaxed into drowsy contentment.

Meanwhile the fuel in the cellar was set alight and fires were banked up all around the house. One by one the servants and attendants stole from the house until the last one. He closed the door after him; and seven strong chains were fixed to it and fastened to the seven pillars of stone. Then fifty smiths came and with their smiths' bellows blew the fire to furnace heat.

Bricriu was the first to speak about the heat:

"We are being roasted from below and above and all around us. And the door is closed fast."

"We shall soon find the reason for that," said Trisgatal, and struck the door mightily. But it held fast, and the only result was the jeering laughter of those outside.

"This is a fine banquet you have prepared for the men of Ulster," said Bricriu to Cuchulainn. "You have led us into an enemy trap."

Cuchulainn rushed to the door and plunged his great sword up to the hilt through the door.

"Iron covered with wood," he said.

"Worse than ever," said Bricriu. And there and then a quarrel would have arisen amongst the men of Ulster because of Bricriu's venom but for the efforts of Sencha.

Outside, the hosts were waiting until the Ulstermen should be overcome by the heat before attacking. A weakness indeed came upon those within; but Ailill and his seven sons stood with their

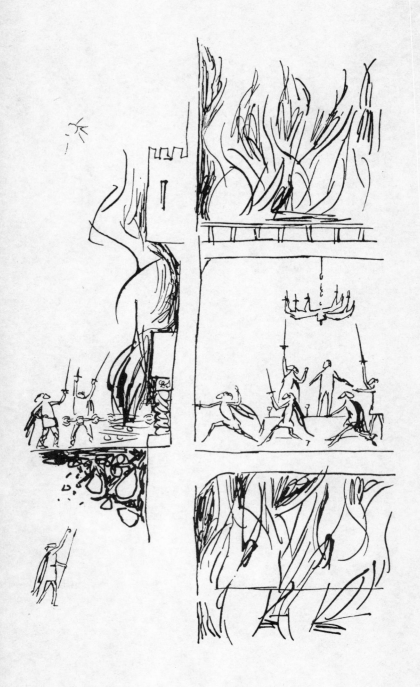

backs to the door and protected them until the heat subsided and the weakness passed. Bricriu then spoke again:

"Cuchulainn brought us here. Let him bring us out again."

Cuchulainn, at his word, advanced and turned a somersault upwards, and carried away part of the roof of the house as he leaped to another roof. A second leap and he was beside the sons of Ailill, who guarded him from fierce attacks while with a mighty heave he broke the fastenings of the door and opened a way for the men of Ulster.

"Now, men," said Cuchulainn, "put your backs to the wall and heave."

And they pushed over the wall of the house, so that three hundred of those outside were killed beneath it.

So the great battle began, and it lasted until noon of the following day. But the men of Ulster were overwhelmingly outnumbered and were forced to give ground. Ailill, seeing this, shouted:

"The stories of the men of Ulster were worthy to be told me until today. 'Twas said that there were not in Ireland men to match them. But today I see them for cravens."

At this the fury of battle came on Cuchulainn, and he assailed the enemy. Conor's son Furbaide was at his side and attacked as fiercely. The men of Ulster took heart and broke the enemy hosts, and when they had wearied of killing they plundered and ravaged the fortress, so that from that time Tara Luachra was no more inhabited. But they spared Ailill and his sons because they had protected them in their weakness.

One of the enemy who escaped from the battle was Crimhthann Niathnair. He met a woman satirist, Richis, who asked him:

"Was my son killed?"

"Yes," he replied; "but come with me and help avenge him."

"What vengeance?" she asked.

"The slaying of Cuchulainn," he replied. And they made a plan.

They came up with Cuchulainn and Laeg, his charioteer, alone by a ford. Following their plan, Richis undressed until she was completely naked and advanced towards Cuchulainn. He turned his gaze to the earth and would not look up at her.

"Attack him now," she shouted to Crimhthann.

"He is coming at you," shouted Laeg.

But Cuchulainn said: "While the woman stands before me in that state, I cannot look up."

Laeg therefore lifted a huge stone and hurled it at her, so that her back was broken and she fell to the ground dead. Then Cuchulainn attacked Crimhthann and slew him.

Laeg had the chariot ready, and Cuchulainn leaped into it and away with him after the rest of the men of Ulster; and they all arrived safe at Cuchulainn's fort, where they feasted for forty nights.

Ailill and his sons were with them and were nobly entertained and loaded with precious gifts. Then they went to their own country in peace and unity with the men of Ulster. And Conor was confirmed in kingship over the men of Ulster while he lived.

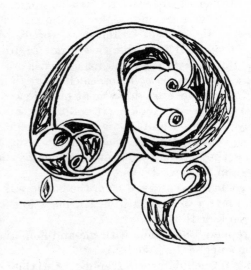

CHAPTER VIII

Etain

WHEN Conor Mac Nessa was king in Ulster, and Mesgegra in Leinster, and Cu Roi Mac Daire in Munster, and Maeve and Ailill in Connacht, one of the high kings of Ireland was Eochai Aire...m. In the first year of his reign Eochai sent out the usual invitation to the men of Ireland to come to celebrate the feast of Tara. But the men of Ireland replied as one that they could not come to Tara for the feast until the high king had a wife. For, they said, there was not one good man of the men of Ireland who had not a wife suited to him, and no king who had not a queen; and no man would go to Tara without a wife, and no woman without a husband.

So Eochai sent his messengers through the land to find him a proper wife, whom no man had had to wife before. They found one whom they thought suitable at Inver Cichmaine, Etain, the daughter of Etar, king of Eochrai; and they told Eochai of her.

The king himself set out with a company to visit her, and as they approached the house of her father they saw her at the edge of a well. She was washing herself from a basin of silver, on the rim of which sat four birds of gold, and round which were precious stones shining. Around her was a bright purple cloak, adorned with silver brooches and caught at the throat with a golden pin. Her tunic was of green silk with a border of red gold, and from the clasps of gold and silver at her breasts there flashed upon the men the colours of the silk and the gold of the sun. Her hair was in two long tresses of yellow gold, and as the king came forward she reached her two arms clear of her cloak above her to unplait the tresses, so that she might wash her hair. And whiter than the snow of one night, or the froth of the waves of the sea, was her skin; redder than the foxglove her cheeks; greyer than hyacinth her eyes; her mouth beautiful and regular; her teeth shining like pearls.

So beautiful was she that to Eochai it seemed she must be of the fairies. He bade his company wait, and went forward and addressed her:

"Tell me, O maid, who are you, and whence?"

"I am the daughter of the king of Eochrai, of the fairies," she replied.

"Will you accept my love?" he asked.

"That is what I wait for," she replied. "It is twenty years since I was born in the fairy fort, and the men of the fairies, and kings and heroes, have courted me, but none has won me, because of my love for you. Since I was a child I have loved you, and my love has increased with the years as I heard the tales of your beauty and valour, and though I never saw you before, I knew you when you came to me today."

"For this," said the king, "you will have all my love, and will be preferred by me before all women, and with you alone I shall live as long as you have me in honour."

"Is my bridal gift ready?" was her reply.

And Eochai brought forward the seven bondmaids to be her gift and she went with him to Tara, where there was great rejoicing at her coming. And the great feast of Tara was held.

Now Eochai had two brothers who were there, and one of these was Ailill Aonglonnach, or Ailill of the One Stain; for the stain on his character was that he fell in love with his brother's wife.

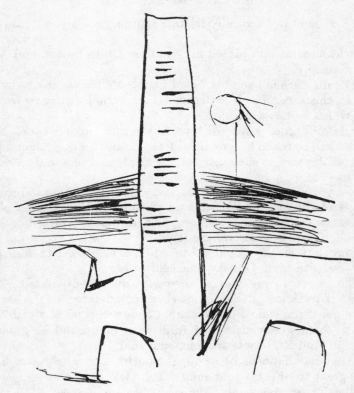

Indeed his own wife, the daughter of Luchta Laimdhearg of Leinster, noticed it at the feast of Tara. For she said to him:

"Ailill, why do you keep gazing to the side so long? Such long-looking is a sure sign of love."

And Ailill was ashamed, and looked no more at Etain while the feast of Tara lasted. But he was consumed with passion for her, and he fell ill, and remained in his illness for a year, yet told no one of the reason for it. And Eochai was worried about his brother and came to see him. He placed his hand upon Ailill's breast and Ailill heaved a sigh.

"You do not appear to be seriously ill," he said to Ailill. "How are you affected?"

"On my word I do not know, but I feel worse every day and night that passes."

89

"I will send my own physician, Fachtna, to see you," said the king.

Fachtna came and placed his hand on Ailill's breast, and Ailill sighed deeply.

"The illness is not serious," said Fachtna, "but it may be incurable in this case. He is suffering either from jealousy or from a love which he has concealed."

And Ailill pined away for love, but confessed to no one. Now Eochai had to make his circuit of Ireland, and he was reluctant to leave his brother in such distress; for he seemed like to die. So he said to Etain:

"Let you stay here, while I am away, and look after my brother with tender care until he dies; and when he is dead, have a pillar tombstone erected to his memory, and his name inscribed on it in ogam." Then he went on his circuit.

Every day Etain would go to Ailill, and attend to him and converse with him. One day she said to him:

"We grieve to see you so sorrowful and so distressed. And indeed if we knew of anything which could bring you relief we would get it for you. But we cannot even tell what ails you."

Now these words distressed Ailill even more, and he groaned heavily. And Etain was troubled and said:

"What has happened to you, O youth? For surely you have some great trouble on your mind. Tell me."

"Blessing on you, Etain," he said. "I cannot speak."

"You sigh and groan heavily, as though your heart was troubled."

"My heart is sick, and so my body is sick."

"Were it even a multitude of fair women, we should bring them to please you."

"Alas, it is but one woman, and I may not have her."

"She is given to another?"

"She is my brother's wife."

Etain gazed at him in silence: for she had given her love to Eochai from the days of her childhood, and no other could ever enter her heart. But she was full of pity for Ailill.

And as for him, now that he had broken silence, the words tumbled from his lips.

"O maiden beautiful, it would be easy indeed for you to cure my illness. It is a love that goes deeper every day, it is a weakness in violence, it is the four ends of the earth, it is boundless as the sky, it is a strangling of the neck, it is a fight against shadows, it is drowning in the waves of the sea, it is a way to heaven, it is the echo of all the love of the world. . . ."

Etain left him that day in sadness and silence. She came again as usual each day after, and though no word was spoken his silence said again all he had said to her. And she grieved to see him dying on her account.

One day as she looked on him with tears of pity in her eyes, he begged her:

"Consent to meet me but once in secret somewhere, and I shall rise from here cured and well. Let me come to you. Yield to me but once."

And Etain in pity for him consented, and arranged to meet him near her own strong house in a secret place. So all that day Ailill looked forward eagerly to the morrow's dawn when he would meet her. And he did not sleep that night, until near the dawn; and then he fell into a long deep slumber.

Etain went to the place at dawn, and she saw coming towards her a man in the shape and form of Ailill, but when he spoke she knew it was not the king's brother.

"Who are you?" she demanded of him angrily.

"I have been sick with love of you since the feast of Tara," he replied, "yet not until now have you consented to come to me."

"Not to you did I consent to come," she replied, "for you are not Ailill, the king's brother. And not for lust did I consent to come, or for desire of another than the king whom I love."

"To me indeed you came. For it was I who put my love for you in the heart of Ailill, and the sickness of my love in his body, that I might be near you and win your love through him."

"Who are you then?" asked Etain.

"I am Midir of Bri Leith," he replied, "one of your own fairy people. Come with me and we shall be happy for all ages together. It would be a dishonour for you to leave one human and go to another, indeed, and even though it were for pity, you would have dishonoured the king to meet his brother. But there is no dishonour to come away with me for ever."

"My love for Eochai, the king," said Etain, "is for ever. And no reward of happiness could persuade me to leave him. Farewell." And she left Midir.

When she returned to Ailill she found him awake, refreshed, and cured of his illness. She told him all that had happened. And when Eochai returned from his circuit they told him also; and he praised his wife; and they all rejoiced at the happy ending of their troubles.

CHAPTER IX

Eisirt

LONG before the time when Fergus Mac Roi was king of Ulster, there reigned in Ulster another king named Fergus, Fergus Mac Leide. And while Fergus Mac Leide reigned at Emain Macha the king of the Lepra and the Lepracan was Iubdan, son of Abdan.

Now these two kings gave a great banquet on the very same day and at the very same hour; and each was surrounded by his heroes and champions.

At the banquet of the Lepra and the Lepracan there were present: the strong man of the kingdom, Glomar, son of Glas, who could hew down a thistle with one stroke of his axe, whom no twelve men of the realm could wrestle to a fall; and the king's heir-presumptive, Beg, son of Beg (which means Little, son of Little); and the king's poet and artist, Eisirt, son of Beg, son of Buaidgen; as well as other distinguished Lepra and Lepracan. (The Lepra were little people, and the Lepracan were even smaller.)

93

Next to Iubdan sat Bebo, his queen, and at his other side sat Eisirt.

As the banquet proceeded their tongues were loosened by sweet old ale, and mirth filled the hall. In the midst of the merriment Iubdan arose and called for attention.

"Have you ever seen a king who was better than I am?" he asked.

"Never," said they.

"Have you ever seen a strong man who was better than my strong man?"

"Never."

"Have you ever seen horses or warriors better than mine?"

"Never. On our word, never."

"On my word I say it, it would go hard with any army which would try to take captives or hostages from this hall tonight."

At this last remark Eisirt the poet burst out laughing. Iubdan turned on him angrily and demanded to know why he laughed. And Eisirt replied that any one man of the fighting men of Ulster could take hostages and captives from all four companies of the warriors of the Lepracan.

"Seize him," cried the king. "He shall pay dearly for that insolence."

Immediately Eisirt was seized; and in the arms of his captors he spoke solemnly to the king:

"Iubdan, for my arrest this night you yourself will spend a year and a day as a captive in Emain Macha, the headquarters of the men of Ulster, and when you return from there you will leave behind you the most precious of all your possessions. And I shall barely escape drowning in the drinking cup of Fergus Mac Leide, king of Ulster. If you grant me three days and three nights of freedom to go to Emain Macha, I shall bring you proof that what I have said is true. If I should fail in this, then you may do as you wish with me."

The king was sobered by the solemn speech, and granted the request. And Eisirt went and dressed for the journey. His shirt was of smooth and delicate silk, his tunic, scarlet and gold broidered, fell in soft folds, his shoes were of pale bronze and gold. Over all he threw his cloak of silk, and took in his hand the pale bronze baton of the poet.

The guard at the gate of Emain Macha was amazed when he

saw the little fellow, so handsome and so elegantly arrayed, but so small that near half of him was concealed in the close-cut grass of the green.

Closing the gate, he went and reported to Fergus and the company at the banquet what he had seen. And one of the company asked him if the visitor was as small as Ae, the dwarf poet of Ulster, who could stand comfortably on the palm of a warrior. To which the guard replied: "On my word, this one would have room and to spare on the palm of Ae."

So all, laughing, demanded to see the little man; and Eisirt was bidden enter. But such was the force of their breath as they laughed and shouted that he begged that only Ae should approach him; and on the poet Ae's palm the poet Eisirt entered. To Eisirt, Ae the dwarf was a giant.

Now the company had feasted and drunk and were merry, and Fergus bade the cup-bearer give to the little guest to drink.

But Eisirt said: "Of your meat and your drink neither will I touch."

And Fergus said: "For that remark you will be dropped into the cup and thus with your whole body you will drink."

At the word the cup-bearer closed his hand on Eisirt and dropped him into the cup, where he splashed and struggled, swimming on the surface of the wine. And as he struggled he shouted:

"Poets of Ulster, will you let me drown, when you have such need to know what I have to tell you?"

When they heard this they lifted him out and dried him and cleaned him.

"Why did you refuse to share in our banquet?" asked the king.

"I will tell you," said Eisirt, "on condition that I come to no harm if you are not pleased."

"No harm. I promise," said the king.

"Listen then," said Eisirt. "While you make love to your steward's wife your foster-son does likewise with your queen."

"Little man, you are no child," said Fergus. "You speak true of me: so I accept the truth of your whole statement."

"Thank you. I will now partake of your meal. For you have admitted your offence. Do not commit it again."

So the little poet became merry, and sang a lay of his king,

Iubdan, and of his comely, brave people. In return the company plied him with gifts, so many that the tallest warrior present could not have been seen behind the mound of them.

Eisirt said: "This is a noble recompense, but I need it not: for no man of the followers of Iubdan has need of anything."

The warriors, however, would not take back the gifts: for it was against their custom. So Eisirt divided the gifts, two-thirds to the poets and scholars, and a third to the stable boys and jesters. And he spent the three days and three nights of his freedom in Emain Macha, and when he was leaving, the poet Ae asked to accompany him.

"I shall not invite you," said Eisirt. "Then, if you are treated well amongst us, you will be grateful; if not, you will not be disappointed, as you would be had you come by my invitation."

On their way they came to a vast sea, and Ae was troubled as to how they would cross it. Eisirt asked him: "What do you see coming over the wave?"

"A russet hare," said Ae.

"Not a hare," said Eisirt, "but Iubdan's horse." The little horse had a mane of crimson and legs of green and a long curled tail. The two poets mounted and came in time to Ma Faithlenn, where the Lepracan shouted a welcome to Eisirt and the giant who bore him company.

"No giant is he," said Eisirt, "among the men he comes from; for on the palms of their hands he stands as it were an infant. His name is Ae, the poet. And now upon you, Iubdan, I place *geasa* which no warrior may break, that you go yourself to see the place where I have been, and that there you be first to taste the porridge which this night is being made for the king of Ulster."

The king was troubled at the *geasa*, and when he told his queen, Bebo, she agreed to accompany him on his visit to Ulster.

They, unlike Eisirt, entered Emain Macha unseen, and Bebo bade Iubdan find the porridge spoken of by Eisirt, and taste it and depart before the people of Ulster woke. But when they found the cauldron Iubdan was unable to reach into it from the ground. So Bebo held his horse while he climbed on its back. Even so, he was still unable to touch the handle of the ladle and, leaning too far forward, he fell into the porridge and was held fast up to his middle in it.

"What delays you, dark man?" asked Bebo from the ground.

(She called him "dark man" because he was raven-haired while all his people were fair.)

"Flee, Bebo, flee," he cried, "for morning is at hand, and I am held as in chains."

And she reproached him, like a woman, for the rash word which he had uttered to Eisirt, and which was the beginning of all his trouble.

"Rash indeed was the word," he moaned, "and for it I must now spend a year and a day here as a captive, and when I depart leave behind me my dearest treasure."

As they talked, she on the ground and he in the porridge, the people woke, and soon there was a crowd around them, roaring with laughter at their plight. At last Iubdan was picked out of the porridge and brought to the king.

"This is not the man who was here before," said Fergus. "That one was fair-haired, but this fellow has a black thatch. Where do you come from, manikin?"

"I am of the Lepra. I am their king. My name is Iubdan. This is my queen. Her name is Bebo. I have never told a lie."

"Put him with the rabble, and guard him well," ordered Fergus.

"Please grant me a favour: put me not with rabble," begged Iubdan. "For the force of their breath overpowers me. I have never told a lie: and I tell you I will not leave here until I am permitted by Ulster and by you."

So Iubdan was granted fair treatment, and a servant to minister to him, and he lived there free of all supervision. And his words and his company gave pleasure to all the men of Emain Macha.

One day he was visiting at the house of a soldier who had just got a new pair of shoes. The soldier tried on the shoes, and as he walked up and down the floor he began to mutter angrily that the soles were too thin and would be worn out in no time at all. Iubdan began to laugh.

The king, who was with him, asked: "Why do you laugh, Iubdan?"

"I am laughing at this fellow, who is complaining that his new shoes won't last long, and yet he has never a complaint about his life. For thin as the soles of his shoes are, he'll never wear them out."

Iubdan was right. Before nightfall that soldier and another fought and killed each other.

And in many incidents like this Iubdan showed his extraordinary powers. But he kept his word and did not attempt to leave Emain Macha.

In time the Lepracan came to Emain in seven companies to seek his return. To Fergus and the men of Ulster they said: "Restore our king to us and we will pay a ransom."

"What ransom?" asked Fergus.

"We will cause this great plain to be covered every year with a rich harvest of corn, without ploughing or sowing. For that will you restore our king?"

"No," replied Fergus.

"Very well so," they said. "Tonight you will pay for your refusal."

"How?" asked Fergus.

"We will bring all the calves of Ulster to their mothers, so that in the morning there shall not be in the province even one baby's share of milk."

"So much you will have achieved," said Fergus, "but not the return of Iubdan."

In the morning they offered to undo the damage if Iubdan were returned. But Fergus still refused. They then threatened to defile the wells and the rivers of the whole province.

"A slight inconvenience," said Fergus; "and it will not restore your Iubdan."

On the third day again Fergus refused, and on the fourth. And they threatened and wrought further damage. They burned all the mills and kilns of the province and they snipped off the ears of all the corn. And on the fifth day they threatened: "We will shave the hair of your men and your women so that for ever they will be shamed."

And Fergus cried out: "If you do that I will kill Iubdan."

At this, Iubdan begged to be permitted to speak to his people: "You have heard the king. Do no more damage lest I die. But depart, having undone all you have done. Do you not remember Eisirt's prophecy that I must stay here a year and a day, and departing leave here my most precious possession?"

So they did as he commanded them; and at the end of the year he bade Fergus choose one from his many possessions.

"They are all precious," he said; and in a long poem he enumerated them: his shield, his sword, his helmet; his cloak, his shirt,

100

his belt, his tunic; his cauldron, his vat, his mace, his horse-rod; his timpan; his needle; his porkers; and his shoes—shoes of white bronze which took their wearer over land and sea alike.

Fergus listened to the poem of praise and pondered. For, whatever their virtues, Iubdan's possessions were of a size suited to the Lepracan. But he thought that if the shoes would even fit on one toe of each foot they would be a fine possession. So he placed a toe in one of them and the shoe stretched until it fitted his foot. And thus Iubdan lost his finest possession, and the prophecy of Eisirt was fulfilled, so that Iubdan could return to his people. The men of Ulster missed the little king and his pert ways when he left, but were consoled by the return of the dwarf poet Ae, who in wonderful lays told them of his adventures amongst the Lepra and the Lepracan, where he was hailed as a giant, and where the king's cup-bearer would lie in his sleeve, where seventeen pretty women would rest on his bosom, where four men would sleep in his belt, and another, unknown to him, in his beard. And the adventures of Iubdan and Bebo and Eisirt at Emain Macha were told and retold amongst the Lepra and the Lepracan to the delight of generation after generation.

CHAPTER X

The Infatuation of Muircheartach
Mac Erca

MUIRCHEARTACH, first Irish high king from the northern line of Niall, had a palace at Cletech, on a bank of the river Boyne. Here he would leave his queen, Duaibsech, daughter of Duach of Connacht, and go off on hunting expeditions.

One day when he was out hunting he was, as it happened, left alone on top of the mound from which it was his custom to view the hunt. As he turned, intending to speak to one of his companions, he saw instead a woman of such breathtaking beauty that he could not utter a word. He gazed spellbound on the brilliance of her fair tresses, on her clear rich-white skin, on her queenly figure, as she sat smiling, her green cloak draped around her gracefully on the mound. In that moment he knew that he would gladly lose everything to possess her.

When he found speech in the warmth of her smile he bade her welcome and asked her name.

"I am the beloved," she answered, "of Muircheartach Mac Erca, king of Ireland. I came here to be with him."

Surprised and gratified, the king asked: "You know me?" And she replied: "You and all the men of Ireland: for I have secret knowledge."

"You will come with me, then?"

"I will, if in return you offer me the reward I seek, O king."

"I will offer you what you have already, all power over me."

"Your word on that."

The king gave his word.

"The clerics will not approve," she said, smiling.

But the king declared passionately that he was hers completely.

"You shall have cattle," he said, "a hundred from every herd, a hundred drinking horns, a hundred cups, a hundred rings of gold, and banquets every second night in the palace of Cletech."

But she laughed at his impetuosity.

"I desire them not," she said. "You have asked my name, and three things I do desire, that you never utter my name, that your queen, the mother of your children, be never seen by me, and that no cleric ever enter the house I am in."

"It would be easier for me to give you my kingdom. Even so, your desires shall be granted. But tell me your name so that I may never chance to utter it."

"My name is Tempest, and all the sounds of storm and wind of the night and winter," she replied.

Without word the king assented and beckoned, and she took his hand and rose, and they went together to the palace. There they found bustle and gaiety as the staff went about their duties cheerfully and the nobles of the house of Niall came in from the hunt in high humour for the evening's feasting, and the shimmer of the westering sun on the salmon-filled Boyne was reflected through the glad house.

Tempest praised the beauty of the palace, and the king was pleased; and without regret, for he was infatuated, he carried out his pledge to her at once; and sent away his queen and their children and all their noble court, the men and women of Clann Eoghain and Clann Conaill, of the line of Niall.

The Queen Duaibsech went with her children to Tuilen to her confessor, the holy Bishop Carnach, and tearfully told him all that had happened. He went with her then and met and consulted with the nobles who had been expelled from the palace of Cletech with their queen. Now the bishop was a man of peace, and well versed in the ways of the human heart, and he persuaded the queen and the nobles to return with him to Cletech so that he might act as peacemaker and convince the king of his sin.

But Tempest reminded the king of his pledge, and he in his desire of her was blind and deaf to all the world, and he barred all entry to the bishop and those who accompanied him. At which the bishop, holy man though he was, became exceedingly angry, and cursed the house at Cletech and all who should ever be under its roof; and as a sign he made a grave on the earthwork for the king.

The nobles in awe of his solemn curse came to him and said: "We are not guilty in this matter. Give us therefore your blessing, O bishop, that we may go our ways." The bishop then blessed them, and they went home each to his own place.

But when Carnach returned to his monastery he found there a great host of the descendants of Tadhg, son of Cian. They had come to seek the holy man's intervention in their feud with the high king and the line of Niall. They wished to end the feud, and they begged the bishop to go with them to the palace at Cletech so that they might make a solemn treaty and peace with Muircheartach. And Carnach, being a man of peace, returned to Cletech accompanied by the descendants of Tadhg.

The king came out of his stronghold and greeted them in friendship, but when he saw the bishop he blushed with embarrassment and asked: "Why have you returned here, O cleric, so soon after cursing us?"

"I have come to make peace," said Carnach, "between you and the descendants of Tadhg, son of Cian."

At this the king showed his relief by ready agreement, and the blood of both sides to the treaty was mingled in one vessel, and Carnach blessed the agreement, saying a short life and hell for all eternity on who should break it. But Muircheartach grudged the time spent away from Tempest, and as soon as the ceremony was completed he bade the bishop depart and not return unless he was summoned.

Inside the palace Tempest awaited him beside his throne, and the king returned eagerly to the delights of her embrace. And wine and her beauty intoxicated him, and every word she spoke was a pearl of wisdom to him.

"You hate the clerics," he said to her. "Do you believe in their God?"

"He exists. I believe that," she said. "But there is no wonder he could work that I could not work its equal."

He clasped her to him and fondled her, and whispered: "Tell me. Tell me of the wonders you could work."

"I could create a sun and a moon, and stars without number. I could create men and beasts. I could make the Boyne a river of wine."

As her voice spoke her boasts, he listened as in a trance; and when she ceased, he spoke dreamily: "For me, for me you must work these great wonders."

"Look then!" she said. "Men! Fighting men! Do you see?"

"I see."

"What do you see?"

"I see two companies of men. And they fight. They slaughter. They maim. They bruise. They pant. They sweat." He roared in exultant enjoyment. "Let us drink. Come, another wonder. Here is water of the Boyne. Turn it to wine."

Tempest smiled her ravishing smile, and he drank and vowed it was the sweetest and the strongest wine he had ever tasted. But she brewed him an enchanting wine from ferns and he luxuriated in its effects and called for meat and drink of her creation for all the host.

Outside the palace the descendants of Tadhg, son of Cian, lay awake listening to the shouts of the king and his praises of the wonder-working Tempest, and they made the sign of the cross on themselves and prayed: for they knew of no hosts that could be within to make sense of the king's words. And they sent a messenger to summon Carnach.

By morning all was silence within. All strength seemed to have left the king, and he remembered the grave on the earthwork. But Tempest beguiled him and gave him to drink, and he was refreshed and called for more wonders. And she pointed and said:

"See, of those stones on the plain I make blue men, and of these other stones men with goats' heads. Go arm yourself and slaughter them."

Out he went in full battle-dress, roaring like an angry bull, and

laid about him, and to his eyes as they fell each one rose up again to fight with him. Thus all day he spent himself charging about the plain doing battle; and at evening in great weariness went in again to the palace and begged for the magic meat and wine to refresh him.

When morning came after his heavy sleep he was so weak that he could scarce stand. But he heard shouting from without, of hosts challenging him to fight. So, wearily he donned his battle armour and going out saw on the plain two companies, one of blue men, the other of headless men. Again he charged against them, stumbling and falling exhausted and rising again with hoarse cries of defiance. And thus engaged did the clerics sent by Carnach find him.

106

"Why, O king," they asked, "do you hack at the stones and sods and the stalks?"

"Your bishop cursed me," he replied. "Shall I take the word of his clerics that these are not men?"

"Put Christ's cross before your eyes and then look," they said. "These are stones you fight."

In a little while he was calmed by their words. "Why did you come here?" he asked.

"To meet your corpse," they said. "For death is near you."

He made the sign of the cross, and confessed his sins, and told the clerics to relate to Carnach how he had repented. Then he dug the first sod for a church to be built on the plain, and the clerics set themselves quickly to complete it, so that they might spend the night in prayer.

The king went back into the palace and sat down without a word. Tempest was startled by his appearance and asked why he had left the fight so early in the day.

"The clerics came," he replied, "and put the sign of the cross over my eyes, and I saw nothing but fern and stone and puff-balls. There was no one to fight; so I came away."

Immediately Tempest began to upbraid the clerics, whose only purpose, she said, was to separate the king from her and spoil their pleasure.

"You have ceased to desire me," she said. But he protested passionately, and she beguiled him again so that on the days and nights which followed he continued as before, until the seventh night, which was the eve of the Wednesday after Halloween. That night there was the sound of a great wind outside, and the king said to Tempest: "The sigh of a winter-night wind."

"You have uttered one of my names," she answered, and immediately without warning there came on such a snowstorm that the king was terrified and his sleep was fitful. Suddenly he awoke, screaming.

"What is it?" cried Tempest.

"A host of demons come to attack me, burning the palace and slaughtering my people."

"'Twas but a dream," she said, soothing him. But he could not sleep again. So he rose and went out to the little church, where a light was burning and the clerics kept vigil in prayer. He spoke long with the clerics, but they could not overcome the despair of his heart. Yet his mind was easier when he returned, so that he slept. Again he woke screaming, to find Tempest gone. She was at the gates.

"Who is there?" he shouted.

"Tuahal Maelgarb, son of Cormac, son of Niall of the Nine Hostages. He is come to take vengeance on you for the battle of Granard."

He ran out and saw a host before him. Back again he ran for his arms, but this time as he came to the door he was met by flames and smoke, nor could he find shelter or safety from the fire wherever he ran, until he came to a cask of wine. And there they found him, five feet of his length burned and the rest of him preserved from the fire by the wine.

He was buried at the monastery of Tuilen, and Carnach recounted his former greatness, before his infatuation. Duaibsech, his wife, made bitter lament for him, and the heart in her breast burst and she died, in grief for her king and husband. So in death she joined him again and they were laid side by side in the grave.

As Carnach and his clerics moved from the graveside they saw a woman, alone, moving to meet them. She was graceful and fair and wore her gold-and-green mantle with queenly dignity. Her head was bowed in sorrow. Carnach recognised her as she came close.

He spoke gently: "You used your beautiful body to ruin a king, and bring shame on his house. What was your terrible purpose?"

Weeping, she answered: "Muircheartach Mac Erca killed my father and my mother and my sister at the Battle of Cerb, on the Boyne, and destroyed the power of the older race at Tara."

"And you hated him?"

"My own father was no dearer to me than Muircheartach, son of Erca. I shall die of grief for him and the harm I wrought him. I came with purpose to ruin him. Too late I knew I loved him. Now I have come to you to confess."

She made her confession and the penance enjoined upon her, and she straightway died of grief. And a grave was made for her by the orders of Carnach and she was laid in it.

CHAPTER XI

The Exile of Colmcille

COLMCILLE was on a visit to Finian of Moville, the pupil visiting his teacher, a friend visiting a friend; and there was great gladness on both of them, but especially on Finian. For Finian had acquired on a journey to Rome a copy of the new translation of the gospels written by Jerome, and was now the proud possessor of the only copy in all Ireland of this accepted version of the gospels. Proud indeed he was, more proud than a holy man of God ought to be.

And never did he indulge his pride more than when he was showing his treasure to his friend. Colmcille was entranced, for he was both a scholar and a poet; and the simple beauty of the Latin was a joy to his soul.

But as well as being a scholar and a poet, Colmcille was one of the most distinguished and most diligent scribes in all Ireland; and as he gazed on the pages of Finian's precious copy his mind was seeing other pages in his own lovely script, illuminated and decorated with all the copyist's art, which was then coming into fashion in Ireland. And his fingers itched for the quill.

"Finian, friend of my soul, this is a treasure indeed. My will congratulates you, but my heart envies you."

"I forgive your heart, Colm: for my own will is humble in thanksgiving, but my heart is proud."

"And who wouldn't be proud of such a possession? They will come from the four corners of Ireland to see and admire it. And copies of it will bring light and consolation to every tuath. 'Tis the treasure of the west you've brought back to us from your journeyings."

Finian moved his fingers across the open pages lovingly, and his manner was abstracted as he spoke:

"Yes. Copies will be made. But not yet. Men must come to see it first, and study it. Moville will be a place of pilgrimage, a shrine for this treasure. And then . . . fitting copies will be made, shining in gold and colour. Copies of the Moville gospels they will call them. . . ."

"No, Finian. Now is the acceptable time. Let the good seed be broadcast now. The ground is ready. Why wait?"

"Colm, Colm. Always impatient. Just a little while, and then you will be the first to copy it. That I promise you."

Colmcille protested vehemently against the delay; but Finian was adamant. No copy would be made until he gave his permission, and no permission would be given yet. The book might be looked at, and admired, and studied. And Colmcille might study it at leisure; for he might take it to his cell and keep it that day and all night until the next morning. But no copy might be made.

The book was taken to Colmcille's cell, and he shut himself in, and was not seen at recreation time that evening; though all the community were eager to see him; for his conversation was lively, and his speech was eloquent, and his intellect so keen that the most difficult problems seemed easy when he explained them.

And as he was not with them they talked of him, and the miracles and wonders which attended his presence everywhere he went. And they talked of his holiness, which was so great that no prayer of his ever went unanswered; and especially they told of each Thursday when, it was said, he was rapt up to heaven in ecstasy. And they talked of his fasting and his austerities, and so

110

on; and indeed there were so many wonderful things about him that they would have talked of him for ever.

And one young monk, who had lately joined the community, was filled with longing to see Colmcille and be in his wondrous presence; and he carried the desire with him to sleep, and when the bell for office woke him, he was filled with it still. So, when the others filed into their wonted places in the chapel to recite the divine office, he stole away to Colmcille's cell: for Colmcille had not come to chapel at the bell.

As he drew near, he saw brilliant rays shining from every chink in the door; and he tiptoed forward, and through one of the chinks he saw Colmcille at his desk, writing. And he was near to fainting with wonder at all else he saw, so that he did not notice Colmcille's pet crane, which came and pecked at his eye through the hole. He screamed with pain, and ran screaming to the chapel, and the monks ran from the chapel at the noise and gathered round him, as men do, some asking what had happened, and some seeking to comfort him, and no one the wiser until Finian laid his hand on him and healed his eye, and bade him say what had befallen him.

Tremblingly he began, but as he told his tale he found courage and confidence in the wonder he had seen and in the rapt attention of the monks.

"And as he sat writing, I saw the source of the beautiful light which came from the cell. The five fingers of his right hand were like torches not burning yet ablaze with light, and the light made the colours of the page flash like burnished bronze in the noonday sun. . . ."

Finian thundered his interruption.

"Stop. Stop. Did you say writing? Writing! If he has dared. . . ."

And he strode from the company and rushed to the cell, the whole company following, aghast at the anger that was on their abbot.

As Finian burst open the door, Colmcille was sitting back, wearily rubbing his tired eyes with a hand that no longer flashed fire.

"So this is how you return my trust in you?"

"I am sorry, Finian." Colmcille spoke wearily.

"You would have deceived me. You copied my book secretly. You have betrayed your word."

113

"I gave no word. I made no promise. Please, Finian, let us not argue about it now. You are angry and I am tired. We shall only quarrel if we talk of it. Let us sleep on it."

"And have I not cause to be angry? You have abused my hospitality. You have stolen my book!"

"No, Finian. Here is your book, unharmed. I take only my copy. Your treasure is still yours."

"You cunning schemer. Give me that copy."

Colmcille was weary, and his temper, not too good at the best of times, was rising. He replied emphatically:

"The copy is mine. I made it."

Finian, too, was in a temper.

"Do you refuse to give me the copy of my book?" he asked through clenched teeth.

"I most certainly do," replied Colmcille. "If it weren't for your selfish pride, you would see that you are but standing in the way of God's work and the spread of His gospel."

Finian was hurt by this, but unrepentant.

"Very well, then," he said, a little more calmly. "The matter will go to the court of the high king."

But Colmcille stalked off with his copy, shouting over his shoulder: "It can go wherever you please, but no force will make me surrender the work of my hands to a selfish, vainglorious abbot."

And Finian, equally silly, as men are when they've lost their tempers, shouted after him: "We'll see about that."

So the matter went to Tara, to the court of Diarmuid, high king of Erin. And the lawyers searched the law books, looking for precedent and enactment. For the one set of laws applied to the whole of Ireland, and those who guarded and preserved the legal tradition were held in high esteem; and the king, as judge, gave weighty consideration to the opinion of the lawyers. But this case was a puzzle. For the lawyers argued that the copy of a book was a child of the parent book, and as such belonged to the parent book. And Finian held steadfastly to this opinion in his claim to the ownership of the copy made by Colmcille, adding that the copy had been made secretly and without his permission. But Colmcille put the lawyers and their finical opinions to one side and argued on the merits of the case and its importance to the community.

"I hold," he said, "that Finian's book is none the worse for my

114

having copied it. And I hold that it is against justice that the word of God which the book contains should be left in obscurity, or that I or anyone else should be prevented from reading it, or copying it, or spreading it amongst the people. And I hold that the benefit I got from copying the book should be passed on to the people, and that neither Finian nor his book would suffer in consequence."

But Diarmuid, for his own reasons, whatever they may have been, gave his now famous decision: "To every cow its calf; to every book its copy. To Finian therefore belongs the copy."

And Colmcille cried out: "It is an unjust judgment, and you shall pay for it."

And while his anger was smouldering an incident fanned it to flame. Curnan, the young son of Ae, king of Connacht, was with the high king as a hostage from his father, and it happened in a game of hurling that Curnan quarrelled with another boy, who was son of the chief steward of Tara. And in the quarrel Curnan struck the other boy with his hurling stick, and the boy died as a result of the blow. Curnan in his terror fled to Colmcille, and the high king ordered that Colmcille should deliver him up for punishment, which was death.

Colmcille in his wrath cried: "I will go to my kinsmen, to Clann Conaill and Clann Eoghain, and rouse them to punish these two unjust judgments."

And indeed he had little need to rouse his kinsmen. For they were already seething at the decision regarding the book. For they said that the high king's decision had been a deliberate insult to Colmcille and to them, and had been given for political reasons: inasmuch as Diarmuid was both jealous and afraid of the power of the northern kingdoms; and further that one of themselves, even Colmcille himself, if he would accept it, ought by right to be high king of Ireland.

So, unknown to and unseen by the high king, Colmcille slipped through the guards and the ambushes set by Diarmuid, and came to his people. And they made ready for battle.

And the leaders were Ainmire, son of Seadna, son of Fergus Cennfeda, son of Conall Gulban, son of Niall of the Nine Hostages, king of Clann Conaill; and Fergus and Donall, sons of Muircheartach, son of Muiredach, son of Eoghan, son of Niall of the Nine Hostages, kings of Clann Eoghain; and Ae, son of Eochai, of

Tir in Charna, king of Connacht and of the Ui Maine of Connacht, and father of the boy Curnan to whom Colmcille had given sanctuary.

And Colmcille fasted on the eve of the battle and prayed to God to give victory to the allies over the high king, and to cause no hurt to his kinsmen. And as he prayed through the night there came to him Michael the Archangel. And Colmcille grieved bitterly when he heard what the angel had to say. For he said that while no prayer of Colmcille's would go unanswered, nevertheless his prayer was ill pleasing to God, and for it Colmcille would be punished. And the angel further said that no one of Colmcille's kinsmen, save one, should be injured: and he enjoined that no one of Colmcille's following should cross the stream that ran between the opposing armies; for anyone of them who should cross would be slain.

So the battle of Culdrevana began: and Colmcille at the rear of the host prayed to God. And Michael the Archangel, a shield on his shoulder and a naked sword in his hand, fought in the van, routing the hosts of the high king. But Colmcille besought God that the high king should not be slain: and he was protected from death.

And Finian at the rear of the high king's host prayed also; but Colmcille sent him a message to say that while he prayed King Diarmuid would not yield, and that his prayers were but prolonging the battle and adding to the number of the slain on King Diarmuid's side. And Finian, knowing that Colmcille's word was always true, ceased to pray. And King Diarmuid's army was routed and three thousand of his men slain. But of the allied soldiers there was slain only one, who crossed the stream against the command of the angel and Colmcille.

King Diarmuid, however, was not deprived of his high kingship: for Colmcille deemed him sufficiently punished for his unjust judgment. But the book over which the battle had been fought was given into the keeping of Clann Conaill; and it was enshrined in silver and gold. And Colmcille prophesied that if it were borne thrice round the host of Clann Conaill, before they went into battle, by a cleric free from mortal sin, they would return from the battle safe and triumphant. And so it came about.

But Colmcille was stricken with grief and remorse. Even from the moment the archangel had spoken to him his heart began to be

116

eaten with sorrow, and when he thought of the numbers which his stubborn insistence on justice and revenge had sent to an untimely death he felt no penance could be great enough to wipe out his guilt.

And he went to Molaise, a holy man who lived as a hermit on the isle of Devenish in Lough Erne, and revealed to him the troubles of his soul. And Molaise placed on him a penance, the like of which he had not thought of even in the depths of his remorse: to leave Erin, and to behold her land no more, nor her men or women, nor tread on the soil of Erin for ever. And Colmcille wept bitterly his "Amen".

And taking with him a company of bishops, priests and other clerics and learned men, he went to found a monastery on the island of Iona, to be the centre of a mission to those parts.

His heart was heavy and sorrowful as he set out on the sea from his beloved Derry, and he made a song:

> *There is a grey eye*
> *will look back on Erin*
> *nor ever see again*
> *her men or women.*
>
> *Many the tears, as*
> *I look back on Erin,*
> *in my soft grey eyes*
> *as I gaze o'er the brine.*
>
> *At early and even*
> *lamenting I go my way,*
> *and tell you my secret name:*
> *"back-turned-to-Erin",*
> *"cul re hErin",*
> *"back-turned-to-Erin".*

Thus the story-tellers relate the exile of Colmcille to Iona: but Eunan, his biographer, says only: "In the second year after the battle of Culdrevna, in the forty-second year of his age, St. Columba, resolving to seek a foreign country for the love of Christ, sailed from Ireland to Britain."

CHAPTER XII

The Death of King Diarmuid

DIARMUID, high king of Ireland, had slain the king of Dalriada, Suibhne, and had taken Suibhne's son, Hugh, who became known as Black Hugh, to rear and educate in his own household. And the druid Beg Mac De, before he died, made a prophecy about these two, Diarmuid and Black Hugh. It happened this way.

The king and Hugh were conversing in front of the king's house at Tara when Beg came up to them and said:

"I see the valiant wolfhound which will destroy this fair house."

"What hound?" asked Hugh, who thought the old man was doting.

"Yourself, it might be," answered Beg.

"How could that be?" asked the king.

"You will easily see that when the time comes," answered Beg.

"And how shall I come to die?" asked the king.

"In the house of one Banbhan," answered Beg, "dressed in a

shirt produced from one flax seed, and a cloak from one sheep, drinking ale brewed from one grain, eating bacon from a pig that was never farrowed, crushed by the main beam of this house."

And Diarmuid laughed at the impossible circumstances of his death. But he ordered his magicians to be sent for, that he might compare their prophecy with the words of Beg Mac De.

Beg Mac De was deeply offended that the king should seem to doubt his powers, and he departed in anger, which was not lessened by the jeering taunts of the young men, who shouted such questions as: "What is the thickness of bacon fat this year, Beg?" after him. And he went to his great friend Colmcille.

Now Colmcille had foretold that Beg, who, although he was still a pagan druid, had the gift of prophecy from God, would twice prophesy falsely before he died. Colmcille therefore said to him:

"Beg, you have great wisdom and knowledge, and often tell others of the time and manner of their death. What have you to say of your own death? When will it happen?"

"In seven years from now," replied Beg.

"A man might do good works in a shorter time than that," said Colmcille. "Are you certain you have that much time left?"

Beg was silent for a while, then spoke:

"No. It is only seven months."

"Are you certain of that?" Colmcille pressed him.

"No," he replied again after a silence; "the truth is I have but seven hours. And since I have twice prophesied falsely, all my other prophecies are true and it behoves me to make my soul."

And Colmcille attended him from that moment until he died, so that he went straight to Heaven.

But Diarmuid, unaware that Beg had in the meantime made the two false prophecies, having ordered his magicians to him, asked them the manner of his death; and though no two of them made the same utterance, nevertheless the sum of all their words was exactly what Beg had said, except for the cryptic reference to Black Hugh.

The king was very puzzled; but he took immediate precautions on such parts of the prophecy as were intelligible to him. He banished Black Hugh from Ireland, on pain of death if he should ever return. And the main beam of the house he had taken down, and cast from a boat far out in the sea.

It was the custom for the high king to make a circuit of Ireland

at intervals, so that for a year he would be travelling, from Tara to the south, from south to west, and across Ulster again to Tara, and on his circuit once Diarmuid was visited by a strange warrior. The king inquired of him where he came from.

"Close at hand is my house," he replied. "And I have come to ask the king if he would favour me by spending the night there, accepting my hospitality."

Diarmuid turned to his queen, Mughain, and asked her opinion.

"You know my opinion," she said. "I never accept such an invitation. Neither should you, for ill may come of it."

But Diarmuid was displeased that in the presence of a stranger she should thus appear to make his decisions for him and he said:

"Whether my queen go or not, I shall gladly accept your invitation." And he went with the stranger to his house.

120

When they were seated, a beautiful young woman entered the room, and on Diarmuid's inquiring who she was, his host said:

"This is my daughter, and, since your queen has refused to accompany you here, she will entertain you." And the young woman sat down with the king and made conversation with him while the meal was being prepared.

"Daughter," said the host, "have you raiment for the king?"

"I have indeed," said the daughter, and presented to the king a shirt and a cloak.

"'Tis fit raiment," said the host. "For my daughter has many strange ideas, and she sowed a single seed of flax which increased until she had a long row of flax, and from that was woven the cloth for the shirt. And the cloak is made of the wool of one sheep."

The king put on the raiment and sat down to the meal.

"The bacon that never was farrowed is good," said the host.

"You talk in riddles," said the king uneasily.

"Not so," said the host, "for we took knives to the sow and took the piglings from her alive and fattened them."

"And the ale?" asked Diarmuid.

"Fine ale," was the reply, "brewed from one grain of corn—a grain I found in the crop of a dove and sowed, and it yielded abundantly."

Diarmuid stood up, and looked at the main beam of the house.

"You notice the beam?" asked the host. "And perhaps you think it strange that it should appear so old and the rest of the house so new? But that is easily explained. Once we were out fishing on the sea, and saw that beam floating on the waves, and we towed it to land and used it in the building of the house."

"But you are not Black Hugh," said the king, seeking to reassure himself.

"Black Hugh is here," said a voice from the doorway, and as the king turned to the voice a spear was thrust through his chest and smashed his spine.

The house was surrounded already, and now those outside set fire to it, and as it burned the main beam fell on the dying king's head and finally killed him. And the prophecy of Beg Mac De was fulfilled.

CHAPTER XIII

Beg Fola

ONE day Diarmuid, son of Ae Slane, went from Tara to the ford of Trim, accompanied by his foster-son, Crimhthan, and one servant. As they came up to the ford they saw coming towards them over the river a woman of great beauty. Her shoes were of silver-bronze decorated with jewels, her robe of crimson and red gold, her cloak clasped over her bosom with a brooch of gold studded with many-coloured precious stones; a gold collar round her neck; a gold crown upon her head; two black-grey horses in her chariot, with reins of gold and trappings of silver.

Diarmuid asked her where she came from.

"Not far away," she replied.

"And what is the purpose of your journey?" he asked.

"I am looking for wheat seed," she replied; "for I have good soil for it."

"If the seed of this country please you, you may have it from me," said Diarmuid.

"I shall not refuse it if a gift come with it," said the woman.

Diarmuid took the brooch from his cloak and offered it to her. She accepted it and went with him.

At Tara they asked him:

"Who is this woman you have brought to be your wife?"

"She has not given me her name," replied Diarmuid.

"What did you give her as a bride-gift?" they asked.

"The brooch from my cloak," he replied.

"'Tis a little bride gift," they said.

"Let that be her name," said the druids, "Beg Fola, little bride gift."

She submitted to be the king's wife, but all the time she was set on seducing his foster-son, Crimhthann, and he knew not a moment's peace from her solicitations. At length she persuaded him to meet her at sunrise on a Sunday at Cluain Da Chailleach, her intention being to elope with him. He spoke to some of his people about this and they convinced him of the folly of a secret assignation with the wife of the high king of Ireland.

On Sunday morning she left Diarmuid's side before sunrise.

"Why are you rising so early?" he asked.

"An errand I must go," she replied.

"Have you no servants?"

"'Tis that my servants have gone from me, and left some of my things at Cluain Da Chailleach. I should not like them to be lost."

"What things?"

"Seven fine cloaks, with seven brooches to match them, and three crowns of gold."

"But you need not go on a Sunday. A Sunday journey has no good end, unless it cannot be avoided."

"There will be someone from the royal house with me."

"Not with my consent or knowledge."

But in spite of Diarmuid's veto, Beg Fola went with her own handmaid to Cluain Da Chailleach. They continued their journey southward, when they found there was no one to meet them, until they reached Dubhthor in Leinster. Here they were wandering about when night fell, and wolves came. Beg Fola fled into a high tree out of their way and lost her handmaid.

While she was in the tree she saw a fire in the middle of the wood, and came down and went to it. Here there was a young

warrior cutting up a pig. He wore a tunic of bright purple overlaid with circles of gold and silver, and a crown of gold, silver and crystal on his head, with fine threads of gold twining through his hair down to his shoulders, gold bracelets to his elbows, his weapons gold-ornamented. His cloak was brilliant in many colours.

She sat at the fire; but he paid no attention to her until he had finished preparing the pig for roasting. Then he set it on the fire, washed his hands, bestowed as it were a brief glance of curiosity on her and went off. She followed him until they came to a lake.

There was a bronze boat in the middle of the lake, a bronze cable from the boat to the land, and from the boat again to an island in the middle of the lake. He pulled the boat to land, she went on board, he followed her and rowed the boat to the island. They left the boat in a bronze boat-house, and went into a well-built, well-furnished house.

They sat down to a fine meal, and drank just short of intoxication. They were alone in the house and slept together that night; but he lay with his back to her.

In the morning they heard a call:

"Come out, Flann; the men are here."

He rose at once, put on his armour and went out. She arose and went out behind him, and saw three men who were very like Flann in features, form and age. Then she saw four others advancing towards them with shields down ready for fight. They fought until all were covered with blood. Then they parted, and Flann returned to her.

" 'Twas a good fight, and you fought it well," she said.

" 'Twould be good, surely, if it were against enemies," he replied.

"Who fought with you and who against you?" she asked.

"My three brothers and myself against four cousins, sons of my father's brother."

"What is the prize you fight for?"

"This island."

"What is its name?"

"Inis Fedach Mhic an Daill."

"What is your name?"

"Flann O Fedach."

"And is the island worth fighting for?"

"It is a good island," said Flann. "It can supply supper every evening for a hundred men. Last night there were but two on the island, and the supply was for only two."

"Why should I not remain here with you?" asked Beg Fola.

"Because you are wife to the king of Ireland," he replied. "And I am not ready to defend myself against his vengeance. But if I win the island, I shall come for you, and you will be my constant wife living with me. But for the present leave me."

"I must find my handmaid," she said, "if she be still alive."

"She is alive," he assured her, "and is waiting for you at the foot of the tree where you fled from the wolves. She was surrounded by the young deer of the country, so that she would learn nothing of our meeting."

She found her handmaid and returned to Diarmuid just as he was rising from his bed on the same Sunday as she had left him.

"It is well you did not travel on the Sunday against my veto," he said to her.

"I would not dare to disobey you," she replied.

But from that time on she often sang:

> *A night on an isle,*
> *A night in a wood;*
> *No stint of ale,*
> *No stint of food.*
> *A night with a hero*
> *I tried to win;*
> *A night with a hero,*
> *But no sin.*

And no one understood her song.

At the end of a year, on a Sunday, four young ecclesiastics came to Diarmuid's house.

"What is this?" cried Diarmuid. "Clerics travelling on a Sunday!" And he covered his head in his cloak so that he might not see them. For it boded ill.

"Not for pleasure, or unavoidably, do we travel," said they, "but by order of our superior, Molaise of Devenish. This morning a farmer, while herding his cows, saw four armed men on Devenish advancing with their shields down ready for fight: and four others met them and they fought fiercely, and the rattle of their shields and the clash of their arms could be heard all over the island. And they fought till all were killed but one, and he was sorely wounded but escaped death. Molaise buried the other seven and gathered up what they left of gold and silver on their necks, their arms, their hands, their shields, their swords, their spears and their tunics. And it was a heavy load for two of us. And Molaise has sent us to ascertain what should be your share of the gold and silver, O Diarmuid."

"What God has thus sent him" replied Diarmuid, "let Molaise keep. I wish no share of it. But let him use it for a crozier and sacred vessels."

The messengers thanked him and added: "There is more to the farmer's tale."

126

"What is that?" asked Diarmuid.

But before they could answer a wounded man came to the door and stood there looking in. And Beg Fola finished her song:

> *The hero comes*
> *From the island fight*
> *To claim the prize*
> *Of the sinless night.*

Diarmuid understood the song. The messengers spoke on:

"The farmer said that at the fight on the island the wife of the king was present."

Beg Fola went to Flann, and Diarmuid said:

"Let her go with him. For indeed we know not her comings and goings."

Beg Fola went with Flann and never returned.

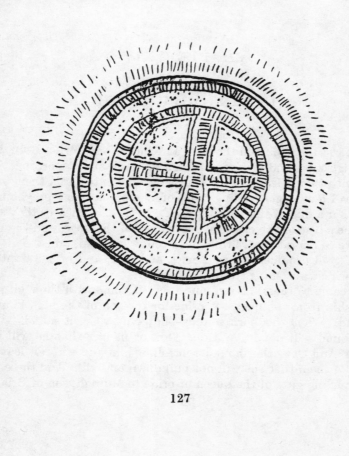

CHAPTER XIV

Brian Boru's Son

SEATED one day on the lawn at Kincora were Brian Boru, the high king, and his sons, Muragh, Donagh and Conor, together with their friends, when they saw coming towards them over the road a stranger leading two hounds, one a noble greyhound, the other a dog of the hunting pack. As he came nearer they saw the fine silver of the chain by which he led the dogs, and the fine texture of his raiment, brilliant in yellow and red, and the gleam of the gold ornaments on his neck and hair, and of the hunting horn which was slung from his shoulder.

He came to them, bowed, and said: "I come with three gifts of courtship from the queen of pride for the son of the high king of Ireland. When this horn sounds—but only when it sounds—this greyhound will not leave a deer, fox or badger that he will not rouse. And this other hound will follow him and will not leave a beast of them that she will not pull down and kill. And these are the courting gifts of the queen of pride to Muragh, son of Brian."

"'Tis no surprise to me," said Muragh, "to get courting gifts from any queen, of any part of the world, but I am a little puzzled to know how the queen of pride heard of my name and fame."

"I will tell you that, O son of the king. One day we were at an entertainment at the palace of the king of Greece, and in the midst of the great host in the banqueting hall the herald arose and shook his chain for attention. In the silence which followed he asked if there were any man, king, lord or earl, of riches and land, of cattle and raiment, who would deem himself fit to court the queen of pride. And there arose one hero, and said he was the man. But I arose and said I had walked the world above and underneath and knew every king, prince and hero, and never had I come across anyone to match Muragh the son of Brian Boru. And so to you, Muragh, come these gifts of courtship."

As he spoke his last word he vanished, like the water of a winter mist or the gust of a March wind.

Next morning Muragh took the horn and the hounds, and with all his company went hunting. And only twice before was there a killing like the killing of that day. When it was finished, Muragh bade his company each to take on him a load and bear it back to Kincora; but they were insulted at being asked to perform such a task, and they went off and left him there alone.

As he stood there at a loss he saw coming towards him the same stranger (though he knew him not) in a very different guise. He was dressed in a short rough shirt and a long plain cloak, and in the crook of his arm he carried three kindling sticks of yew. He bowed to Muragh and said he was a servant in search of a master.

"I need a servant at this very moment," said Muragh. "What wages do you ask for a year's service?"

"To settle my own wage at the end of the year," replied the servant.

"And what special qualifications have you that you should merit the settlement of your own wage at the end of your service?" asked Muragh.

"I am the best story-teller that is, or ever was, or ever will be."

"Flahu, who lived in the reign of Fiacha Finnlui, was the best story-teller who ever lived."

"I knew him well" retorted the servant. "He told of things that were. But the stories I tell are of things that never were and never will be, so that I can soothe to sleep all who are ill or unwell."

129

"And have you any other qualification?" asked Muragh.

"I am the best travelling man that is, or ever was, or ever will be."

"Luailua the crooked, who lived in the time of the Red Branch, was the best travelling man who ever lived."

"I knew him well," retorted the servant. "He could travel round the country in five days; and there wasn't a woman on his journey from whom he did not take a meal. But I can travel the country in one day; and I need take to eat from but one woman, and even that meal I can go without."

"You tell me you remember the time of the Red Branch?"

"I do, and farther back, even to the time of Eremon."

"Faith, you're an old youth," replied Muragh. "Have you any other qualification?"

"I am the best man at kindling a fire that is, or ever was, or ever will be."

"Mac Leisc of the heavy load, who lived at the time Cormac reigned at Tara, was the best man at kindling a fire who ever lived."

"I knew him well," retorted the servant. "He would bring his load of timber from the woods, and he would be cooking with it for seven days and nights, and would sleep after that for another seven days and nights. But I need but three kindling sticks of yew, and with them I could give warmth for themselves and heat for cooking to all that are, or ever were, or ever will be, and still have my three sticks intact at the end of it all."

"If all you say is true," said Muragh, "you are the best servant ever."

"It is true," said the servant.

"Very well, I accept your terms," said Muragh.

"This is a great killing you have here," said the servant. "Why did you not bid your company to bring it back to Kincora?"

Muragh told him what had happened. The servant straightway took some cords from his cloak and tied the whole killing into a huge bundle.

"Help me lift it," he asked Muragh.

"That would be no work for my rank," said Muragh.

"Well, you are the master. I am the servant. I'll lift it myself." And he lifted the load. "Now go ahead and show me the way," he said.

"The master does not serve the servant," said Muragh.

So off went the servant with a leap and a bound, straight to Kincora. And his appearance terrified the guard at the door; and when he threw down his load the palace and the ground all around it trembled. But in no time at all he had the meats cooked and the banquet ready.

He served his master for a full year, and proved the truth of his claims. For he travelled the wide world and every night had a new story to tell, and he did all the work of a serving man and a serving woman. The day after his service was complete he went to Muragh to state his wages.

"For wages," he said, "I want you to put a ferrule on this stick, so that it fit exactly."

"In truth I had expected you to ask more than that for your service," said Muragh.

"I do not think it a trifle," said the servant.

Muragh took the stick to his smith and bade him put a ferrule on it to fit exactly. The smith measured the stick and made a ferrule, but it did not fit. And he made another, and another and another, and he could not make a ferrule to fit the stick. They went round the country to every smith, and none could make a ferrule to fit the stick.

When they were resting beside Loch Derg the servant said: "I may as well tell you no smith in the world could make a ferrule for my stick for there is no ferrule will fit it but the one that was on it before. And 'tis that ferrule I want you to get for me."

"Where is it?" asked Muragh.

"If you will listen a while, I'll tell you," said the servant, and began his tale. "In this very place, beside Loch Derg, there was once a great banquet, attended by the high king of Ireland, the king of the Fian, and the king of Underwave Land, and their followers. And in the midst of them all, the herald rose and, shaking his chain for attention, asked if any of those present had ever seen a board that was better or more plentiful in food than the board before them. And all but myself said, 'Never'. I said nothing. So they asked if there was any food or drink wanting to me, so that they would get it for me. But I told them I neither would praise nor find fault with their feast, for I could praise no food in comparison with the food which came from the cauldron in the land of the Danes. This cauldron needed but to be set on three magic stones and have three kindling sticks of yew set under it in order to feed all the men that were or ever had been or ever would be, and that without anything being placed in it.

"But they laughed and said there never was such a cauldron, until the king of the Fian said I wouldn't tell a lie; and then they said they must go and find the cauldron. So they prepared an expedition, of seven hundred of the Fian, to go with me, and we eventually came to the land of the Danes. There we saw a hill with four roads leading to it and each road guarded by a hundred fierce warriors, and on top of the hill the cauldron with seven hundred fierce warriors at each corner of it, and the people of the country moving to and fro as they were fed from it.

"Now the warriors with me were terrified at the array against them and had no strength to go forward. So I had my head shaved like an idiot or an amadan and went up as if to get my food like the rest of the people there. I waited my chance and at last managed to throw the three sticks of yew and the three magic stones which were under the cauldron into it. Then I hoisted the cauldron and away with me through the glens of the air and out of sight of the gathering.

"They came after me and met my seven hundred warriors and a terrible slaughter began. And I was vexed to see my friends being killed for the sake of an old cauldron. So I threw it from me as far as I could put it and attacked them, and you could still today hear the sounds of the slaughter we inflicted on them.

"We took the cauldron and brought it to the house that was here, but it was too big to come in through the door. So we put it under a big tree with its feet on the three magic stones, and we put the three kindling sticks of yew under it. And then they all admitted that what I had said about the cauldron was true; for it supplied meat cooked and ready for the men and women of Ireland without any thing ever being put into it.

"It was not long then till the men of Ireland were heavy in flesh, from getting their living so easily. But one day a monster came out of the lough and, smelling the meat cooking, made straight for the cauldron and began gulping down the food that was in it. She filled the men of Ireland with terror and they fled from her. Now I thought it was a sorry state of things that the monster should reap the benefit of all the trouble we had had to get the cauldron. So I attacked her with the only weapon I had,

this staff, and didn't the ferrule fly off it into the cauldron, and I had to leap for safety into the tree, while the monster gathered herself round the cauldron and off with her into the lough with it. And that's where my ferrule is, under the lough, in the cauldron."

When he had heard the servant's tale, Muragh, son of Brian, went home and rested that evening. And in the morning he donned his full armour and went to the lough. Leaping into the middle of the lough, he went down until he came to the monster, and casting his great spear cut her in two. Then, closing with her bravely, he cut off her head. And her blood reddened the waters of the lough (it is still called Lough Derg, the Red Lough) so that the people said that Muragh must be dead and his blood upon the waters. But the servant lad said, that if all the people there were slain, and Muragh, and seven times as many more, the waters of the lough would not be so red. "'Tis the monster that is dead," he said; and with that they saw Muragh coming towards them, the monster's head in one hand and the ferrule in the other. He came forward and put the ferrule on the staff and it fitted exactly.

"I have my wages now," said the lad, "but the treasure you left behind you is better than all you brought with you."

"Very well," said Muragh. "I'll know the way better the second time." And with that he dived into the lough again, and brought up the cauldron.

"Now indeed," said the servant, "I really have my wages." And away with him into the lough, cauldron and all.

Muragh was very angry that his people should be so deprived of the benefits of the treasure, and he told the old king, his father, that he was placing himself under *geasa* not to sleep two nights on the same bed, nor to eat two meals at the same table until he had brought back to Kincora the servant, the cauldron, the three magic stones and the three kindling sticks of yew.

"Victory and blessing to you, my son," said Brian.

With the blessing of his father and his mother and his kinsfolk, Muragh next morning, with all his princely armour and equipment, dived again into the lough and travelled underwater for three days and three nights until he came to Underwave Land. He was not long there till he heard a woman's voice raised in bitter lamentation. Now it was Muragh's custom when he heard a woman weeping to seek the cause of her complaint, that he might help.

When he asked her, she replied: "Where were you born, and what land are you from that you do not know my complaint?"

"Eire is my country, and I know nothing of your complaint or your lamentation," said Muragh.

"I shall tell you, then," said the woman. "This country once belonged to the Underwave king, but the five-headed giant and his monstrous hag of a mother took two-thirds of his kingdom from the king, and exacted tribute from him. And the tribute is that every time the giant goes past them, in or out, to give him a maiden every night for his bed, so that he may eat her the following morning for his breakfast. And there are no young women left in the kingdom except the daughter of the king and my own only daughter, who is one of the beautiful women of the whole world. And it is but a few moments since he came here with a cauldron on his back and announced that I must send my only daughter to him tonight. Now, my hero, you know the reason for my complaint and my lamentation."

"Give the young woman to me," said Muragh, "and in the morning I shall go to the giant instead of her."

"You shall have her, and a thousand welcomes," said the woman.

Then the woman told him that it was in the prophecy that Muragh, son of Brian Boru, would come from Ireland and save the country from the giant.

"But I don't know," she added, "whether he is born yet or not, or his father, or his grandfather, or within a thousand years of him."

When Muragh told her who he was, she was overjoyed, and it is a wonder she didn't smother him with kisses or drown him with tears. She gave him the choicest of food and the oldest of drink, and then she brought him to the sun-top of her house, where he saw before him a fair, gentle, beautiful woman, with golden hair, blue eyes and shining teeth. Her skin was whiter than the snow of one night, and her cheek was redder than the royal rose. As she gazed on him, her mother told her who he was. And the maiden welcomed him and made ready a place for him. And then they made three thirds of the night, a third for tales of the Fian and other stories, a third for feasting and celebration, and a third for relaxing in deep sleep.

In the morning Muragh made ready to meet the giant, who was

very annoyed at being disappointed of a maiden the night before, and now had no breakfast. Muragh, therefore, leaving the maiden and her mother sorrowful after him, went straight to the court of the giant and struck three blows on the pole of combat. The great, ugly, five-headed giant came to him and said: "No life or health to you, ugly Muragheen from Ireland. In a moment I am going to tear you apart into little bits."

They attacked one another, like two mad bulls, or two raging lions, or two dragons in the wilderness, or two red hawks in the sky. They wrestled and fought for a day and a night, twisting necks and wrenching heads and cracking bones, with victory to neither, until a voice was heard saying: "Isn't it a great shame for so fine a hero to fall by the hands of an ugly monster, and he so far from home and with no one to keen over him dead."

At that the noble blood rose in Muragh and with a tremendous heave he threw the giant on his back on the ground.

"Your head off you, giant," cried Muragh.

"Off me indeed, if that be your will," answered the giant. "But stay your hand and you shall have from me a spear of victory and a blessing, a horse that will pass the wind in front of it and outrun the wind behind it, a healing vessel, and a multitude of jewels, two-thirds of this kingdom from the day of my death, and I myself shall take the place of a servant boy and a servant girl for you."

"I shall have all that, and your head as well," said Muragh, and with his sword swept off all five of the giant's heads. He put a skewer through the cheeks of the five heads and went with them thus to the court of the Underwave king. There he found his servant of the ferrule seated on a golden throne with a silver cushion beneath his feet, and the three kindling sticks burning before him. And it was a wonder he did not smother Muragh with kisses or drown him with tears. And he gave him the choicest of food and the oldest of drink and invited him to stay a while for feasting and celebration.

After a time the servant of the ferrule, now king, asked Muragh: "How long would you say you have been with us here?"

"A week or two," replied Muragh.

"Do you not know," said the king, "that this is Tir na n-Og, the land of the young, and that you don't notice the time going past? You have been here exactly a year and a day."

And immediately Muragh began to be anxious about his father and his mother and his kinsfolk. But the king reassured him, reminding him of one of his qualifications as a servant, that he was no mean travelling man. Hence he knew all that went on in the world.

"But I know the *geasa*," he added, "which you placed on yourself. So you shall bring me and the cauldron back with you."

"Indeed," said Muragh, "if it weren't for the *geasa* I wouldn't ask the cauldron of you."

"In that case," said the king, "if you promise to return the cauldron to me, I'll go with you to Ireland and bring it back with me." And Muragh promised.

When they arrived at Kincora all the nobles of Ireland gathered to meet them and there was great rejoicing and feasting for three days and three nights.

At the end of the feasting Muragh said: "I have fulfilled my *geasa*, and now I return the cauldron to the servant of the ferrule with grateful blessings: for he was a good servant to me and is entitled to the wages he asked. And maybe it wouldn't be good for the people of Ireland to have the cauldron."

So the servant took the cauldron with blessings and thanks, and off with him back to Underwave Land, where he lives to this day and will live for ever.

CHAPTER XV

The Demon of Gluttony

A GREAT and glorious king of Munster was Cahal Mac Finguine, and a contender for the title of high king of Ireland as well. His rival was Fergal Mac Maelduin, king of Aileach in the north. 'Twas of these two the hag of the south and the hag of the north sang:

> *From the north he is coming, is coming,*
> *Maelduin's son, on a raid for cattle.*
>
> *If Cahal meets him, Cahal of Munster,*
> *He'll be lucky to escape alive from the battle.*

To complicate matters there was a great love between Cahal and Fergal's sister, Ligeach, though neither had ever seen the other. (That was a common thing in those days.) Anyway Ligeach used to send sweets and apples to her love, Cahal, and it was this that caused all the trouble. For Fergal came to hear of it and sent for her one day.

139

"A blessing on you for the truth," he said, "and a curse on you for a lie. Now tell me, what is this I hear about yourself and Cahal of Munster?"

Now the girl loved Cahal much, but she feared her brother's curse more. So she told him all.

"The next lot of apples you have for him," said he, "give them to me; and I'll send them on to him."

The girl did as she was told; and when the apples came to him, he sent for his magician, and explained to him what he wanted. The magician used all his charms and incantations to doctor the apples, and messengers were dispatched with them to Cahal, who accepted them as a token of the love and affection of Ligeach, and ate them all.

And that was his undoing. For inside him the apples generated little creatures, and they formed themselves together into a monster demon of gluttony. And if Cahal had an appetite before of a man, he had the appetite now of a monster. For a snack to take the edge off his hunger, while his main meal was being prepared, he would eat a cow and a calf, and a pig, with thirty eggs and sixty wheaten cakes, and a barrel of fresh ale to wash it all down. As for his main meal, it is beyond telling. And thus was Fergal destroying Munster, and the power of the south, which could strengthen his claim to the high kingship. But indeed he was like to destroy the whole of Ireland as well: for there was no end to the monster's voraciousness.

Now there were eight men in Ireland at that time, of whom poems were sung in praise at Armagh, the great seat of learning and piety; and one of these was the scholar Anier Mac Con Glinne. His power of satire was such that his like was never before or since, and none dare refuse him anything, in fear of his satire. Which is how he came by his name.

On a Saturday evening, as he sat at his studies, a sudden disgust of study seized him as he thought of the wretched life of the scholar and the luxury which might be his if he followed the call of poetry. There and then he resolved to go to Munster and join the court of Cahal of Munster. For he had heard that Cahal was partial to white meats of all kinds, and he himself had a longing on him for white meats.

So he sold all his possessions for two wheaten cakes and a slice of old bacon with one lean streak across its middle, and making himself a pair of shoes with pointed toes, put the cakes and the bacon in his book-bag, put his book-bag on his back, grasped his well-balanced, knobbly staff, which was five spans from end to end, in his hand, went by the right around the cemetery, bade farewell to his master, who said protective incantations over him, and off with him to Munster; and did not stop till he was at the guest house of the monastery in Cork. It was a long tramp.

The guest house was open when he reached it and the wind swept through it: for it was a day of the three things, snow and rain and wind. And the vat for bathing was beside the door, with the previous night's water still in it. The bed was unmade, and the blanket on it alive with fleas and lice.

There was nobody to wash the guest's feet. So he washed them himself, and his shoes as well. Then he lay on the bed and was eaten by fleas and lice, so that he could not sleep. He took his psalter from his bag, and sung his matins and lauds and psalms and hymns and antiphons and lessons, and paters and canticles in tens and fifties. And the singing of his voice was heard in every house in Cork.

Manchin the abbot of Cork was in his bed. He called his attendants. He asked:

"Is there anyone in the guest house tonight?"

"There is not," said one attendant.

"I saw one go there," said the other.

"Go to him, and bring him his allowance," said Manchin.

The attendants went to the guest house with the allowance, which was a cup of whey-water, two sparks of fire in a wisp of oat-straw, and two damp peats. It was pitch dark. They stood at the open door and shouted:

"Is there anyone within?"

"There is one," answered Mac Con Glinne.

"We are under *geasa* not to prepare the house for only one," said they.

"The *geasa* are violated," said Mac Con Glinne, "and I am the man who violated them. So you may safely prepare the house."

"Rise, then, and eat your allowance," said they.

"I've waited for it a long time," said he, "I'll wait now till I see what you have for me."

They blew the sparks and lighted the straw so that he saw his allowance. When he saw it he composed a satire on it; and refused it.

The attendants brought the allowance back to Manchin and recited the satire to him.

"If the man who composed that be not punished," said the abbot in a rage, "the verses will be sung against us."

"How will he be punished?" they asked.

"Strip him and whip him and douse him in the Lee; then take him back naked to the louse and the flea. He'll repent in the morning his verses of scorning, and learn that he's tried us too far; for tomorrow we'll try him and then crucify him, in honour of me and the church and St. Bar."

It was done that night as he said, and in the morning Manchin and his monks gave Mac Con Glinne a trial, and every man of them in order of rank from the first to the last spoke against him with legal learning and wit, but out of the laws they could find no point on which to crucify him. He craved a favour before execution.

"Is it your life?" asked Manchin.

"That is not what I ask, though gladly I'd have that also," he replied.

"Tell us then," ordered Manchin.

"I need guarantors and securities for its fulfilment," he said.

They were given.

"Now tell us your favour," said Manchin.

"To eat, before going to my death, my food for the journey. It is in my book-bag."

The book-bag was brought to him and he took from it the two cakes and the slice of bacon. He cut off a tenth part of each.

"It is my custom," he said, "to give a tithe to those poorer and more wretched than myself."

All the beggars of Cork rose up on hearing this, and stretched out their hands. He looked them over one by one and said:

"As God's my witness, there's not one of you poorer or more wretched than myself. Yesterday I tramped from Roscommon to Cork. Did any of you tramp so far? Not a bite had I on the road, and not a bite since I came, as a guest, to the monastery. Did any of you suffer like that? Hounds, thieves, excrement, you monks of Cork; you stripped me, you whipped me, you doused me in the Lee. It would be a first charge against me when I die if I gave tithes to any of you, for you do not deserve them."

So he ate the tithes himself and then the rest of his viaticum.

"Now to the execution," ordered the abbot.

"A favour for us," cried the monks.

"You, too," cried the abbot. "What is it?"

"We are weary," said they, "and still have all the good works of the Sunday to perform. Let the execution wait till the morrow."

"Let him be stripped again, then," said the abbot, "and bound to the pillar there, and let him fast for his sins till morning."

So it was done, and the monks went off to their good deeds, and they fed the poor, and they fed themselves, of course, also. But Mac Con Glinne fasted, naked in cold night air. And an angel of heaven came to him and sat on the pillar beside him. But that made the pillar too hot; so he asked the angel to move away from him a little. And the angel sat on a ridge near him. (That is the origin of the name Angel's Ridge in the green of Cork.) In the morning the angel left him.

The abbot came, with his monks, and asked him:

"Well, wretch, how do you feel now?"

"Fine," said Mac Con Glinne. "I had a vision last night, and I'd like to tell you about it."

"There'll be no more delays," said the abbot.

"We'd like to hear about the vision," said the monks.

But first Mac Con Glinne traced Manchin's pedigree back to Adam:

> *Your blessing, abbot, fount of learning,*
> *Son of lard, son of herring,*
> *Son of porridge, son of curd,*
> *Son of liquor (glorious word!),*
> *Son of bacon, son of butter,*
> *Son of fruit in shining cluster,*
> *Son of wine, son of ale,*
> *Son of mead, son of kale,*
> *Son of sup, son of bite,*
> *Son of cheese, son of tripe,*
> *Son of kidney, son of sausage,*
> *Son of soup, son of pottage,*
> *Son of gravy, son of drip,*
> *Son of back, son of hip,*
> *Son of pure new milk of sheep,*
> *Son of nut, son of wheat,*
> *Son of every part of cattle,*
> *Son of Abel, son of Adam.*

"Your pedigree is original, Mac Con Glinne," said the abbot coldly, "but it has no effect upon me. Are you finished?"

"That is but the prelude, according to custom," said Mac Con Glinne. "The vision follows."

And he related the vision:

> *The vision that befell*
> *me last night I'll now tell*
> *in the presence of all.*
> *We rowed 'cross Lough Milk,*
> *on a surface smooth-silk,*
> *in a lard boat small.*
>
> *Our journey was quick*
> *to the custard thick*
> *which protected the fort.*
> *The wall was of wheat,*
> *the door was of meat*
> *of every sort.*
>
> *Away at the rear*
> *was a fountain of beer,*
> *a pool for each taste.*
> *Beside it a wood*
> *of sweet apples, a food*
> *that ne'er goes to waste.*
>
> *The chief I espied*
> *with his wife by his side*
> *enmantled in fat.*
> *And last but not least*
> *the server of the feast*
> *sat by his vat.*
>
> *Now Cahal, good king*
> *might like me to sing*
> *my vision's short tale.*
> *But one hour 'twould take*
> *to tell of Milk Lake*
> *and the day we set sail.*

When he was finished the abbot Manchin spoke:

"Last night I too had a vision, and it was revealed to me that

Cahal Mac Finguine would be cured of his malady by a vision such as you have related. Go to him therefore at once."

"If I go," said Mac Con Glinne, "what will I get as a reward?"

"Aren't you getting your life?" said the abbot. "Is that not enough for you?"

"That is no great matter," replied Mac Con Glinne, "for the gates of heaven are wide open for me, and all the faithful from Adam and his son, Abel, down to the faithful soul which went to heaven this moment as I spoke, and the Cherubim and Seraphim, all are singing in joy of my entry into heaven—which they expect any moment from your hands. So it won't worry me if Cahal of Munster and all the men of Munster, and especially all the men of Cork, not least of them the abbot Manchin, should die and go to hell tonight. For myself I shall be united with God in the unity of the Father and the Son and the Holy Ghost."

"Well, what reward do you want?" asked the monks.

"Not much," replied Mac Con Glinne. "Only the abbot Manchin's little cloak."

"Not much to you," said the abbot, "but a lot to me. And I tell you before God and St. Bar that if I owned all County Cork, I'd sooner give it to you than that little cloak."

"Woe to him who refuses the cloak," chanted the monks, "for the salvation of Cahal and Munster has priority over the cloak."

"Well if it is to succour Cahal and Munster, he may have it. But I won't give it to him. I'll give it to the bishop of Cork, and he may give it to him."

So the bishop got the cloak; and kept it. But Mac Con Glinne went to the house of Pichan of Iveagh. And Cahal came there with all his company, so that Pichan was out of his mind with worry about the demands of the king: "I would sooner feed the great hosts he has brought with him than feed him alone," said Pichan. "I have to prepare for him a bushel of oats, and a bushel of apples, and a bushel of wheaten cakes."

And indeed when they arrived they had scarce sat down, and scarce was one thong of Cahal's shoe loosed, before he began stuffing apples into his mouth with both hands. When he saw this, Mac Con Glinne began smacking his lips noisily to attract the king's attention, but Cahal took not the slightest notice of him. So intent was he on stuffing himself.

Mac Con Glinne then went to the great stone on which rivets were fastened and weapons ground keen, and lifting it on to his back went and sat facing the king. Then he placed the huge stone on his knees and began chewing at the top of it and grinding his teeth on it. And the noise he made was heard far and wide.

Cahal looked up from his eating for a moment, and said: "That is a silly thing to do, son of learning. Why do you do it?"

"Two reasons," said the scholar. "One, to wit, that Cahal, fair son of Finguine, high king of the southern half of Ireland, principal defender of Ireland against the descendants of Conn the Hundred Fighter, ordained by God and nature king, should be eating alone. The other, to wit, that if any stranger came into the hall tonight, he would jeer not to see my beard go up and down in harmony with yours."

"You're right," said Cahal, and threw him an apple, at the same time stuffing two or three into his own mouth. And it was remarked that Cahal had not acted so generously with food for three-and-a-half years, since the demon of gluttony took up its residence in him. Said Mac Con Glinne:

"Two is better than one, according to the books." The king flung him another.

"The number of the Trinity." He flung him another.

"The four gospels." Another.

"The five books of Moses." Another.

"The number that is its own parts and fractions—its half is three, its third is two, its sixth is one." Another.

"The seven things prophesied of God on earth." Another.

And so on to "the perfect number, Christ with his apostles." Cahal lost his temper. He took the apples and flung them all at Mac Con Glinne. And he was in such a rage that the eyes began to pop out of his head and as he sat down heavily there was not a part of the hall that did not rattle.

"Why do you behave like this?" asked the king of Mac Con Glinne, in a temper.

"Because last night," replied the scholar, "I was cursed by the monks of Cork. That is the reason."

"You wouldn't have come hither, and you wouldn't go hence if it were my habit to kill scholars," said the king.

"Grant me a favour, please," replied Mac Con Glinne.

"Do you hear?" shouted the king to Pichan; "the scholar wants a favour now."

"Give it," said Pichan.

"I give it," said Cahal. "What is it?"

"When I have securities," said the scholar, "I'll name it."

"Securities granted," said Cahal.

"Your word, O king," asked Mac Con Glinne.

"Granted," said Cahal. "Say your favour."

"Last night the monks of Cork cursed me, because of you, O king. You are my partner, therefore, in the curse. I have to fast this night because of the curse. You must be my partner in the fast also."

"All Munster you may have," said Cahal tearfully, "but not that."

"Your word has been given," said Mac Con Glinne. "And besides, would you have me go to hell's fire everlasting under the curse of the monks, for the fast of one night?"

"There has not been a favour since the beginning of the world," said Cahal, "nor shall be until its end which hurt more the giver than this hurts me. But you will have your favour."

They fasted that night, and with them all the company. Pichan rising from his bed awoke them.

"Why does Pichan rise so early?" asked Mac Con Glinne.

"To prepare a meal for men whose appetite has been sharpened by fasting," was the answer he received.

"Do not be anxious about the meal," said Mac Con Glinne. "After the night's fasting we must have a sermon."

When all were awake, Mac Con Glinne arose, washed his hands, took out his psalter, and preached to them. And annalists and ancients and the books of Cork tell us that there was no one present, of humble or high degree, who did not shed three showers of tears at his preaching.

When the sermon was over, prayers were offered for the king, and the prosperity of Munster, and the usual things for which prayers are offered after a sermon. Then Mac Con Glinne went to the king and asked him:

"How are things with you today?"

"Worse than ever was or ever will be," he replied.

"Just as one would expect," said Mac Con Glinne, shaking his head judicially. "After all, you have had a demon laying waste your interior now for three-and-a-half years. And never once in all that time did you fast a day or a night for your own sake, though you fasted last night for poor, wretched no-account me."

"What is the point of all this, O son of learning?" asked Cahal.

"This," answered Mac Con Glinne; "that we all fast tonight, you with us, to obtain help for you in your ailment."

The two argued again; but in the end the king gave in: and they fasted that night.

In the morning Mac Con Glinne woke Pichan.

"Up with you," said he, "and get me well-cured bacon, and tender corned beef, and a fleshy wether, and a comb of honey, and English salt on silver dish, and four perfectly straight white hazel spits to carry the joints."

All that he asked was brought to him. He put on a linen apron and a linen cap and proceeded to cook the meal, and his speed was as it were of a deer about her first offspring, or of a roe, or of a swallow, or a bare spring wind in the flank of March. When he was finished he shouted:

"Ropes, Pichan."

With the ropes he had Cahal tied to the wall of the palace, secure and immobile. Then he brought in the roast on the four spits and sat down cross-legged in front of Cahal; and taking his knife from his belt he cut a choice morsel and put it into his mouth. He rolled his eyes and smacked his lips in enjoyment of the morsel. Then he cut another and brought it past Cahal's mouth, under his nose, and into his own mouth.

Cahal spoke hoarsely:

"Carve for me, O son of learning."

"I'll do that," said the scholar, and again brought a choice morsel past Cahal's mouth into his own.

"How long are you going to keep this up?" asked Cahal.

"Not long," said Mac Con Glinne. "For I'm very hungry. And it's little enough I have here for myself compared with your meals of the past three-and-a-half years."

Cahal roared and shouted and screamed at this, and strained and struggled at the ropes, and called on his company to kill the scholar. But no one interfered. And he cried out in an agony of desire for the food; but the scholar went on eating.

"And now," said Mac Con Glinne, "I believe you are very good at interpreting dreams. I had a dream which I'll tell you now, and I'd like you to tell me what it means."

"By heaven," said Cahal, "if I interpreted every dream that was ever dreamed, I wouldn't interpret yours."

"Well listen to it anyway," said Mac Con Glinne, and he smacked his lips juicily as he told it: "I heard a voice in my dream:

> 'Danger, danger, all around you.
> Be careful lest the gravy drown you.'

"I heard it twice but heeded it not. And when morning came in my dream the shadowy figure met me.

" 'Hello,' said he.

" 'Hello,' said I.

" 'I warned you last night,' said he, 'but I might as well try

> to look for wool on a goat,
> row a rudderless boat,
> catch water in a sieve,
> without womankind live,
> give warning to a sinner,
> make pepper my dinner,
> brighten a sad man,
> get crops from a bad land,
> feed beer to a baby,
> look for wit in a gaby,
> a silly woman trust,
> or keep a loose one from lust,
> the gospel unpreach
> or Antichrist teach,

as teach you, Mac Con Glinne anything about food.'

" 'Those are hard words,' said I.

" 'Why so?' said he.

" 'I don't know you, or where you're from, or where you're going, so I can't argue with you,' said I.

" 'I'm from the Fairy Hill of Feeding,' said he.

" 'Have you anything new about feeding?' said I.

" 'I have,' said he, 'but you'd have to be a powerful eater to match up to it.'

" 'How so?' said I.

151

" 'Well,' said he,

> *'You'd have to have a belly five spans wide*
> *With room for nine feeds thrice inside,*
> *With seven times nine good helpings of wine,*
> *With seven mastications and digestions nine,*
> *And every feed and drink, and every digestion*
> *Enough for a hundred. Does that answer your question?'*

" 'It does,' said I, 'and I'll listen to your advice. For the belly you have described isn't mine. But first tell me who you are.'

> *'I am Wheateen,*
> *Son of Milkeen,*
> *Son of good fat bacon.*
> *Lard's my wife,*
> *And all my life*
> *She has never me forsaken.*

> *'My daughter's name,*
> *Known far to fame,*
> *Is succulent Cream-cheese.*
> *Corned Beef, my son,*
> *My only one,*
> *In every aspect pleases.*

" 'And now my advice to you is to go at once to the Witch Doctor, who can cure every ailment of the appetite, with the most wonderful, pleasing, palate-titillating, tender, savoury, sweet and choice selection of food and drink you've ever dreamed of. You will be going to his fort at a good time for there is a great celebration there for the completion of his huge pavilion of fat. And all his family and all the chiefs and princes of the tribe of food will be there.'

" 'Put a charm on me, then, and let me go,' said I.

" 'My threefold charm,' said he. 'May fine fat bacon guard you, Mac Con Glinne. May cauldrons of pottage guard you, Mac Con Glinne. May thick, golden cream guard you, Mac Con Glinne. And as you go, invoke the aid of the mighty heroes, the chieftains of food, for

> *there's danger, danger, all around you,*
> *danger lest the gravy drown you.'*

"'Which of these chieftains,' I asked, 'are the strongest protection against the heavy waves of gravy?'

"'The suets and the cheeses, of course,' he replied.

"I went forward, therefore, in good heart, eagerly lusting for the remedy of my disease. I came to a harbour of Lough Fresh-milk and on the lake espied a fine juicy boat of beef, with a coating of tallow, sides of curds, prow of lard, stem of butter, rowlocks of marrow and oars of old boar bacon. A sound craft.

"We rowed across the Lough's wide expanse, through currents of broth, past mouths of mead rivers, over swelling, windy waves of buttermilk, by everfull pools of gravy, past forests dewy with juice of meat, past wells of savoury lard, past islands of cheese, past hard rocks of rich tallow, past headlands of mellow curds, along strands of every kind of cheese. And each time an oar came up it brought a spray of cheese-curd sand. We came at last to the Witch Doctor's abode.

"The door-keeper, Gilla Bacon Mac Gilla Butter, admitted me. I passed the Doctor's son, fishing for all kinds of savoury foods in the lake. Inside the house was a pure white mattress of butter. I sank to my ears in it. The Doctor came to me. I told him my disease, of the longings I had for foods and my inability to satisfy them. The Doctor shook his head: 'A serious disease,' he said, 'but I have the cure for it.

"'Go home now,' said he, 'and wash, and comb your hair, and sit down at a good fire and wait for your meal. And let a woman attend on you, a woman of good repute, and good discourse, her movements graceful and quick, her speech soft and sweet, the melody of strings; no fault, no stain, no blemish on her. Let her give you three times nine morsels, and let you put each in your mouth with a jerk; and roll your eyes as you eat them.' And he enumerated the choice viands from which the morsels should be taken. A heavenly list.

"'And whatever ailment may come on you after that,' said he, 'I'll cure you of it except one complaint, the complaint of nobles and philosophers, the best of all complaints, the complaint of continued good health, looseness of the bowels.' And that is my vision, O Cahal."

As Mac Con Glinne recounted the various foods and drinks of his vision, and as he smacked his lips noisily and rolled his eyes, and spoke so lyrically of sweets and savouries, the demon in

Cahal's interior, was drawn forth and came and sat upon the king's head and licked its lips greedily.

Meanwhile the scholar, during the recital of his dream, was still passing the morsels of food past the king's mouth to his own, and the black eyes of the demon followed each piece hungrily, until at last with a snarl of curses it fixed its claws in a morsel as it went past, and darted to the fireside with it to eat it. And Mac Con Glinne said: "To God and Brigid thanks"; and clapped his right hand over his own mouth and his left over the king's.

"What now?" said Pichan, watching the demon carefully.

"Let everything of any value be removed from the fortress," said Mac Con Glinne.

That was done.

"Set fire to the house," said he then.

That was done.

When the house was one huge flame the demon could be seen on the ridge-tile of it.

"Bow down to me wretch," shouted Mac Con Glinne.

"Since you tell me, I must," said the demon. "For I cannot help it, you being a man with the grace of God, abundance of wisdom, acuteness of intellect, deepest humility; naturally virtuous, with the seven gifts of the Holy Ghost; and I being a demon of indefinable substance. For three-and-a-half years in Cahal's belly I was the ruin of Munster, and was like to ruin all Ireland, but for you. If it were not for the nobility of the monks of great Cork of Munster, for their wisdom, their purity and their uprightness, and for the host of their bishops and confessors, and for the virtue and honour of the revered and noble king you came to save, and for your own virtues and learning, 'tis down your own throat I'd go, and it wouldn't be like the king you'd be, but they'd lash you and whip you through the length of Ireland, and you'd die of the hunger I'd bring you." And with curses and threats the demon flew straight up in the air to join the demons of hell.

They prepared then the last great meal for the king; and sweet music was played to him; and a soft downy bed was made ready for him; and he drowsed into a deep, satisfying sleep which lasted, they say, for three nights and days.

When the king awoke he sent for the scholar, and named his reward, in cattle and kind: a levy from the whole of Munster, and a reward for the story of his vision, to who should preserve it and recite it.

So let the tale be heard as it is handed down, by story-tellers and historians, in the books of Cork. And anyone who listens to it shall hear nothing sorrowful for one year; and the newly-married couple to whom it is told will have an heir, nor shall they want for food and clothing; no corpse shall be borne from a new house in which it is the first tale told: the house shall not want; fire will not burn it; the king to whom it is told before battle shall be victorious; and these are but some of the thirty principal virtues attached to the story.

And he who tells it shall have as a reward a cow with white spots and red ears, a new linen shirt; a woollen mantle with brooch attached, from king and queen, from married couples, and from stewards. . . .

CHAPTER XVI

Young Finn

THE battle of Cnucha was fought for the leadership of the Fian and the head-stewardship of Ireland between Finn's father, Cool, son of Trenmor, and Morna and his sons. In the battle Morna's son, Ae, fought Luchet and killed him; but Luchet had wounded Ae in the eye and he was blinded in this eye: hence the name Goll (one-eyed) by which he was afterwards known. Cool was wounded by the man who was guardian of his treasure-bag, and killed by Goll, who assumed the leadership of the Fian.

Now when Cool was killed, Finn was not yet born, and Cool's friends guarded Muirne, his wife, until the child was born. The child was given the name Demne and was taken away to a forest of Sliabh Bloom to be nursed and cared for by two women warriors. They reared him secretly, for the sons of Morna were ever searching for him to kill him. But the women kept him safe from harm.

One day the boy went out alone. He saw a brood of ducks on a lake and taking a stone threw it at them so that he cut the feathers and wings from one of them and dazed her. He took her back with him to the hunting booth where he lived with his women guardians. And that was Finn's first feat of hunting.

Not long after this he went off with a group of craftsmen who were travelling round the country. He was not well cared for by them and was attacked by scurvy, so that he lost his hair. Hence for a while he was called Demne the Bald.

There was a robber at this time in Leinster called Fiacail and he came upon the group one day and killed them all except the boy, whom he carried off with him to his den in a swamp. When the two guardians heard of this they came southwards and found him and brought him back home with them.

But one day he went off alone again and did not stop till he reached the plain of the Liffey. On the green in front of a fort there he saw some youths hurling, and went in amongst them to take part in their games and exercises. And there was no one could excel him in their sports. Next day he returned to them, and they matched a quarter of their number against him. But he won from them. On the third day they matched a third of their members against him. And he won. At last they contended with him all together in a body. And he won the game from them all.

"What is your name?" they asked.

"Demne," he replied.

The youths told this all to the man of the fort.

"Kill him, if you can," said he to them.

"We could not," said they.

"Who is he?" asked the man.

"His name is Demne," they replied.

"What is his appearance?" he asked.

"Well made and fair," they replied.

"Fair (Finn) be his name, then," said he.

And the youths called him Finn.

Next day when he came to them they attacked him with their hurling sticks; but he laid seven of them low and the others fled from him.

He did not come back to them for a week; and when he came they were swimming in a lake. They shouted to him as he stood watching them from the shore:

"Come and see if you can drown us." It was their intention to

drown him; but he leaped in amongst them, and drowned nine of
them. He went back then to Sliabh Bloom and did not return to
the fort again.

One day when he was out on Sliabh Bloom with the women
warriors, a herd of swift wild deer appeared before them.

"It's a pity," said the women, "that we couldn't catch one of
them."

"I could," said Finn, and ran after them; and catching two fine
bucks, brought them back to the hunting booth.

After that he hunted constantly on Sliabh Bloom; and the two
women were in no need of meat. But they realised that Finn was
now ready to set forth alone to make his own life.

They bade him farewell therefore, and told him to be ever on
his guard against the sons of Morna.

He left them and did not stop until he reached Lough Leen, at
Killarney; and he hired himself in military service to the king of
Bantry. He did not tell them who he was, but his prowess revealed
him and the king one day said to him:

"If Cool had left a son other than Tulcha, one would say you were
he. But Tulcha is in Scotland, in service with the king there. Who
are you?"

Finn did not answer; but that day he left and went into military
service with the king of Kerry. One day the king invited Finn
to play chess with him. Finn played and won seven games in
succession.

"Who are you?" asked the king.

"The son of a peasant," answered Finn, "of the Luaighne of
Tara."

"No peasant," said the king; "for you can be none other than
the son whom Muirne bore to Cool. And the sons of Morna seek
to destroy you. So let you be gone from here, lest you be killed
while you are under my protection."

So Finn moved off again and came to the house of a master
smith, Lochan. The smith had a beautiful daughter, Cruithne by
name. She fell in love with the youth.

"My daughter has fallen in love with you," said the smith to
Finn; "and though I do not know who you are, you may take her
as a wife."

"Make two spears for me," said Finn. And the smith made
them.

Finn took the spears and went out. As he went, the smith called after him:

"My son, do not go by the road where the pig called Beo is. For it has ravaged the whole of Munster."

But that was the very road by which Finn went. And the pig was lying in wait and charged at him. But he slew it quickly with one thrust of a spear, and cutting off its head, brought it back to the smith as a bridal gift for his daughter. The hill where he slew the pig is still called Sliabh Muc.

Finn now considered it time for him to seek his uncle, Crimall, the son of Trenmor, who was in Connacht. On his way there he heard a woman's wail. He went towards the sound, and her tears were of blood in drops and gushes, so that her face was red. He asked the cause of her blood-weeping.

"Good cause," she cried; "for my only son was slain by a huge ugly warrior who came in my way."

Finn went at once in pursuit of the warrior, and when he caught up with him fought and slew him. And he found with the warrior the treasure-bag of Cool, his father; and knew that the man he had slain was the man who had wounded his father Cool, in the battle of Cnucha.

He took the bag with him into Connacht, and searched there until he found Crimall in a lonely wood apart. Some of the old men of the Fian kept him company and hunted for him.

Finn stayed with Crimall a little while, and learned much from him of the ways of the Fian, so that he was almost ready to seek his father's place. But there was one thing he lacked, poetry. So they decided that he must go to Finn Eces, who lived at the Boyne.

Seven years Finn Eces had been watching at the Boyne to catch the Salmon of Knowledge. For he knew the prophecy that it would bring all knowledge to the one who should eat it, and interpreted it to concern himself. And indeed he caught the salmon while Finn was with him learning poetry.

Joyfully he handed it to his pupil:

"Demne," he said, "this salmon is all for myself. Cook it well and bring it to me."

Finn brought it to him, well cooked.

"You are certain you did not eat any part of it?" he enquired.

"No," said Finn; then added, for he wished to tell the truth

159

exactly, "but when roasting it I burned my thumb, and put my thumb in my mouth to ease the pain."

"Alas!" said Finn Eces. "Yet you say your name is Demne. Your name should be Finn. For prophecy is that the salmon should be eaten wholly by one called Finn. Now my name is Finn. But you have tasted of the salmon before me. So I cannot eat it wholly."

"I have been called Finn," said Finn, "because I am fair."

"Then you are the Finn of the prophecy," said Finn Eces. "Eat the salmon."

Finn ate it; and that is why whenever Finn put his thumb into his mouth and sang the "song of light", whatever he was ignorant of previously used to be revealed to him.

He stayed with Finn Eces until he had learned all the art of poetry, and before he departed he made a poem to prove his attainment:

> *Maytime, delightful time,*
> *Beautiful its colours.*
> *Blackbirds sing their full song*
> *At slender shaft of dawn.*

> *The cuckoo sings his constant strain*
> *In welcome to the summer.*
> *Bitter winter's gone away,*
> *Thick the forest's branches.*

> *Summer dries the rivers down,*
> *Swift horses seek the pools,*
> *The heather spreads its flowing hair,*
> *The soft, fair bog-down grows.*

> *The startled deer is bounding,*
> *The sea is lulled to rest,*
> *Smooth the water falling,*
> *Flowers cover the earth.*

> *The bee's small strength is loaded,*
> *From the harvest of the flowers.*
> *Muddy the mountain cattle.*
> *Full the ants' feast.*

The forest harp makes music,
The sail fills in peace.
There is colour on the hills,
And haze on full lakes.

The corncrake speaks his poem loud,
The waterfall, a virgin,
Sings welcome to the pool.
Rushes begin talking.

Light the swallows darting,
Loud music round the hill,
Buds the soft mast richly,
Stutters the trembling bog.

Peat is black as the raven,
Loud the cuckoo's welcome,
Leaps the speckled salmon,
Leaps the bounding warrior.

Man's strength is surging,
Maid's fair beauty is proud.
Perfection in the forest,
Perfection in the plain.

At this time Conn the Hundred-Fighter was giving a great annual feast at Tara, and it was the custom, during the time of this feast every year, that there should be a truce of all feuds and enmities.

In the midst of the feasting a young man came into the hall and sat down in the presence of the king and of Goll Mac Morna. The king looked towards him, and taking his horn of assembly placed it in the young man's hands and asked:

"Whose son have we here?"

"I am Finn, son of Cool," was the answer; "I am son to the warrior who held the chief command of the Fian; and I am come in friendship to you, O king."

"You are a friend's son, and therefore a friend," said the king, and took him by the hand and set him beside his son Art, to enjoy the feast.

After a little the king arose, and when he had the silent hearing of all present, announced:

"This is the time when the fairy man, Aillean Mac Miona, woos every man at Tara to sleep with his fairy music, and when Tara is unguarded sets it afire. If there be one among you who can this night and until dawn protect Tara from the fire, to him I will give his rightful heritage now, whether that heritage be great or small."

The men of Ireland were silent. For they knew that no one could resist the sweet melodies of the fairy music, neither women in labour nor warriors gashed with wounds: but that all would fall asleep.

Finn arose and asked:

"Who will be guarantors and sureties to me that I shall have my heritage if I perform this task?"

Said Conn: "The kings of Ireland, and Cithru and his druids." And so the bond was made.

Now there was present a man, Fiacha Mac Conga, who had been in the close confidence of Cool when he was head of the Fian and he came to Finn secretly and made himself known to him. Finn was pleased and promised him his place in the Fian should he perform his task and win his heritage.

Fiacha said: "My boy, if I obtain for you a magic spear from which no cast was ever made in vain, what favour will you grant me in return?"

"What favour would you wish?"

"A third of all your right hand wins," replied Fiacha, "and a third place in your innermost counsel."

"Granted," said Finn, and gave his word to it.

Fiacha brought him the spear and gave him instructions for his task:

"When you hear the fairy music, strip the covering from the spear's head and place the weapon against your forehead."

Finn began his watch at once, and he was not long at it when he heard the first strains of the plaintive melody. Immediately he placed the spear against his forehead, as instructed.

Aillean continued his fairy music until all, as usually happened, were fast asleep. But Finn was awake; and when Aillean ceased his music and sent forth from his mouth the flame to burn Tara, Finn met the flame with his cloak; so that the cloak was burned and with it the earth beneath to a great depth. Hence the valley called Gleann an Bhruit, the glen of the cloak, and the hill beside it called Ard na Teineadh, the Hill of the Fire.

When Aillean saw that his magic had failed he fled at once to the fairy fort on the summit of Sliabh Fuaid. But Finn followed swiftly and with his spear transfixed him as he entered the door of the fort. Finn then beheaded him and brought the head back to Tara and fixed it on a pole for all to see when they awoke.

Aillean's mother made a lament for him:

> *The fairy chief of Ben Boirche is fallen,*
> *Ochon.*
> *By the mantle of Finn and the javelin of Fiacha.*
> *Ochon.*
> *Aillean Mac Miona, chief of Sliabh Fuaid,*
> *Ochon.*
> *Aillean the joyful maker of music.*
> *Ochon.*
> *Nine times he burned down Tara at the feasting.*
> *Ochon.*
> *Famed was his name, but now he is fallen.*
> *Ochon.*

When the company of Tara awoke Finn displayed the head of Aillean, and said to the king:

"Here is the head of him who used to burn Tara. Here is the timpan with which he made his music. Tara is safe. My task is done."

The king called Goll Mac Morna to him and said:

"Finn has won his heritage. What is your choice, Goll, to quit Ireland or to lay your hand in Finn's in fealty to the new head of the Fian."

Goll said: "I lay my hand in Finn's hand, and pledge my fealty."

Thus did Finn succeed to his father's place at the head of the Fian.

CHAPTER XVII

The Hard Man

IT was the month of May, and Finn and the Fian were exulting in the first big chase of the season after their sojourn in winter quarters in hostels all over Ireland since Samhain. According to his custom Finn had a watcher on a high point viewing the progress of the hunt and keeping an eye out for any sign of mischief from the Tuatha De Danann: for they often chose the time when the warriors were scattered in the chase to work some of their magic against the Fian. Now it happened that Finn was resting for a little while, with Oisin his son, and Oisin's son Oscar, and Goll Mac Morna and Caoilte Mac Ronain, and Diarmuid O Duibhne and Conan the Bald. And to pass the time they were playing chess, while Finn Ban Mac Breasal watched from the hill.

Suddenly there was a cry from Finn Ban, and, as they jumped to their feet, scattering chessmen over the grass, they saw him fleeing headlong down the hill towards them, and heard his shouts of terror. But of what had frightened him they could see nothing

166

until he was almost amongst them crying out: "A giant! A giant!"

Then they saw the giant, and even they were startled by his appearance. He was huge but his size gave him no dignity or bearing, for every feature and joint of him was out of proportion. His face was the ugliest ever seen in Ireland, with its thick lips, its long, yellow, uneven teeth; and thick tufts of coarse hair, matted and dirty, growing all over it, and a long thin neck joining his ungainly head to his long body.

His belly was bloated, his legs were thin and knock-kneed. His feet were big and flat and he walked with his toes turned in. He carried two long spears, badly rusted, in his left hand, while by his left side hung a heavy, rusted sword. The shield which hung over his back was battered and broken. But his most terrifying weapon was a huge iron club which he trailed along the ground from his right hand, ploughing a deep furrow in the earth.

As he came round the hill they could see that with a halter in his left hand he dragged behind him a horse which was as large and ugly and ungainly as himself, and as disproportionate in limb and joint. It was a stubborn brute, too, and would plant its flat feet on the ground and refuse to move sometimes, until the giant would fetch it a blow of his club on its skeleton ribs.

Not a word was said among the men of Finn as the giant and his horse advanced slowly towards them. When they reached the spot where Finn stood the giant went down on one knee and saluted the leader of the Fian. Finn then asked him the usual questions, his name and his ancestry, his country, and his occupation.

The giant replied: "Of my ancestry I can tell you nothing for I do not know who my father and mother were. I am a Dane of the north but I live in any country where I can find a king or a noble to pay me for my service. And having heard of Finn Mac Cool as a great and generous and noble master I have come to offer you my service for a year and at the end of that time as is my custom I shall myself determine what wages you shall pay me.

"They call me the Gilla Deacar, the Hard Man, for there never was a servant anywhere who was harder to put up with than me. I am lazy. I grumble at the slightest task that is set me. And I show no gratitude whatever for any kindness that is shown me. You couldn't have a worse servant. And you will find it difficult to get enough food to satisfy myself and my horse. Does that answer your questions?"

"You have given me honest answers," said Finn. "But I cannot believe you're as hard as you say, or indeed as you look. Nor is it my custom to reject a man who offers his service. So I accept you on your own terms for a year."

The giant then turned to Conan the Bald. "Tell me," he asked, "would a man get more pay in the service of the Fian as a horseman or without a horse?"

"The horseman gets twice as much as the man on foot," replied Conan. "Good," said the Hard Man. "I'll be a horseman. But I don't see anyone here that would be good enough to attend my horse; so I suppose I'll have to look after him myself. He's a fine horse, you know; and I wouldn't like anything to happen to him. So I put him under the protection of you, Finn, and of all the Fian who are here."

There was a good deal of laughter at these remarks, but the Hard Man took no notice. He merely announced that he would take his horse and loose him to graze with the horses of the Fian. Which he did.

No sooner was the ugly animal loose among the other horses than he set about every kind of mischief. He kicked them, he butted them, he tore them with his long sharp teeth, until there wasn't a sound horse left in the lot, and some were so badly damaged as to be beyond remedy. And when he had finished that lot, he headed off to where Conan the Bald's horses were grazing apart by themselves.

When Conan the Bald saw this he ran immediately to head him off, shouting to the Hard Man that he would kill the brute if there were no other way of saving his horses.

"You can stop him if you put a halter on him," replied the Gilla Deacar. "Though it's a shame to halter a horse when he wants to graze. But if you're so worried about your horses here's his halter."

Conan was angry at the giant for making a horseboy out of him, but there was nothing he could do but take the halter and throw it over the big horse's head. And that was the limit of what he could do. For the horse planted his feet firmly on the ground, and, in spite of all Conan's efforts—and Conan was one of the strong men of the Fian—did not move an inch from his position.

Conan lived up to his nickname, "the foul mouthed", and yet he dared not let go the halter in case the brute savaged his horses. And while the Hard Man looked on unconcernedly the rest of the Fian found some satisfaction for their own losses in Conan's discomfiture.

At last Fergus Finnbheil, the poet, spoke. "Conan," he said, "I never thought I'd see the day when you would be horseboy to anyone, let alone an ungainly foreigner and his ugly nag. But if you would pause from your cursing a minute, I'd offer you a piece of advice. Why not, since you must keep a grip on the nag, get up on his back and ride him over the roughest country you can find till you break his ugly heart and make him think twice before he tries any mischief again?"

Without a word Conan leaped on the brute's back and kicked and beat him with all his strength: but the horse paid not the slightest attention to him.

Fergus spoke again: "What's wrong I see is this, Conan. He is accustomed to carrying the big fellow here, and he won't move unless he has an equal weight on his back."

And Conan called out: "Come on, then, one of you. Get up here and help me punish this brute for the damage he has done to your horses."

With that Cael Crodha joined Conan on the horse's back. But still not a move out of him. And Daire Donn Mac Morna jumped up also, and then Angus Art Mac Morna, and then others until there were fifteen of them all beating and kicking, on the big horse's bony back. And they had anything but a comfortable seat.

But the Gilla Deacar now showed some anger. "Finn Mac Cool," he said, "I'm afraid all the fine tales I've heard about you and the Fian were lies, and I'll be your servant no longer. Pay me my wages and let me go."

"Oh, no," said Finn. "I engaged you for a year. At the end of the year you will get your wages. I would like you to stay."

"Not another minute," said the Hard Man. "Pay or no pay, I'm going now. And wherever I go I shall tell the truth about Finn and his Fian."

And with his head held high he moved off. The horse, seeing his master move, went after him, the fifteen heroes on his back. And the rest of the Fian raised a mocking cheer for their fifteen companions.

169

But the giant increased his speed and his long legs stretched to an uncomely gallop, the horse galloping in his wake. And Conan Maol and his fellow riders found themselves stuck to their steed so that they shouted for help to Finn.

So Finn and his men went off in pursuit, with Liagan Leimneach, a swift runner of the Fian, in the lead. After a great many miles across the country Liagan succeeded in overtaking the horse and caught him by the tail. But the horse pulled him with him and he too found he could not let go; for his hands were stuck fast to the tail. And thus the Gilla and his horse and the sixteen of the Fian went into the sea which parted before them and closed in behind them until they were lost to sight of Finn and his companions.

They were a weary sad group as they stood on the shore, remembering their mocking laughter at Conan, and now looking out over the empty sea where the bald hero had disappeared. And Fergus the poet was advising that they should go to Ben Edair and take ship in search of their lost comrades, when two young men of noble appearance came forward and saluted Finn. They were arrayed in scarlet and gold and fully armed. Finn asked them the usual questions and one of them replied:

"I am Faruach and this is my brother, Foltlor. Our father is king of Innia. We have come to you because of your great reputation for wisdom, so that you may settle a dispute for us, namely, which of us practises the better art. We should like you to take us into your service for a year and at the end of the year give us your judgment."

"What arts do you practise?" asked Finn.

"When there is need," said Faruach, "I can provide a ship for any company, with only my carpenter's axe and my stone-sling, if the company will but cover their eyes while I strike three blows on my sling with my axe."

"And I," said Foltlor, "can follow any track to its end, whether on land or sea."

"You have come to me just when I need you," said Finn, and told them his need. And Faruach produced a beautiful ship in the way he had told them, and it was fitted and ready for a long voyage.

Meanwhile Finn had sent out a call for all the Fian to come to him. And on the advice of Oisin and Oscar and Goll he decided to take

170

fifteen men with him in pursuit of the giant. And he left Oisin in charge of the Fian, to defend Ireland, in his absence. Among those who went with him were Oscar and Goll and Diarmuid, and Fergus Finnbheil, as well as Faruach and Foltlor.

Foltlor followed the track of the Gilla Deacar, in light and darkness, in sunshine and cloud and through storm and tempest, for many days, until they came to a cliff that rose sheer and precipitous from the floor of the sea to the clouds above. And there the track ended: so it was clear that whoever would follow the giant must go to the top of the sheer cliff: and that seemed impossible.

But the tongue of the poet Fergus came to their aid, as he spoke tauntingly: "Our comrades are somewhere on top of that rock. They are prisoners. And there is no one to rescue them though we have with us a warrior who is not only skilled in all the arts of fighting but has learned much of magic lore from Manannan Mac Lir amongst the Tuatha De Danann and from Angus at Bru of the Boyne. It's a pity he would not think of applying his skill and his prowess to the rescue of his comrades."

Diarmuid was stung by these reproaches, which were directed at him, and arose and armed himself, and planting his two spears firmly he vaulted on them into the air and found a grip far up on the cliff. As the clouds cleared they followed his progress up the face of the cliff until he waved to them from the summit, and moved from the edge out of sight.

He walked forward through a fair country, a flowered plain surrounded by rich-leaved trees, and birds and bees making the air sweetly loud. Before him was a ring of tall stones round a tall tree. Beside the tree he saw a well and beside the well a very tall stone. The well was crystal clear, bubbling with inviting spring water, and Diarmuid, thirsty after his exertions, bent forward eagerly to drink. As soon as he did so he heard a noise as of an armoured host coming to attack, and he sprang up to defend himself, but saw no one. Nor did he hear a sound, save the singing of the birds and the humming of the bees.

Completely at a loss he shrugged his shoulders and bent forward again to drink, with the same result as before. This time he was in no doubt that he had heard the noise, and he examined his surroundings very carefully to see if he could discover the source of it. On top of the tall pillar beside the well he saw a drinking horn, decorated beautifully in enamel and gold, and he thought to himself: "The noise I heard was a warning. If I drink from this well it must be from the drinking horn." And now he was able to drink to his complete satisfaction without interruption.

But when he was finished and had replaced the horn, he was challenged by a huge warrior, fully armoured and ready for battle, who strode angrily into the ring:

"Have you not enough of spring water in Ireland, Diarmuid O Duibhne, that you come to my country and without permission drink from my well, using my drinking horn? Well, this very instant you shall pay for your arrogance."

With that he charged furiously. But Diarmuid matched him and coolly parried his thrusts until each had the measure of the other and a grim hot fight began. And it lasted till sunset, with advantage to neither.

In the failing light suddenly the huge warrior leaped from the combat into the well and disappeared into its depths. Annoyed and frustrated Diarmuid stood looking down into the well. He had intended to overcome his challenger and bring back with him to the Fian some trophy to support the story of his hard fight. And he was very angry at being foiled.

However, it was time to eat and rest. So he went off to the forest on the edge of the plain where he had noticed the movements of a herd of deer. He had no difficulty in spearing one of them, for he was an unerring marksman; and he cut off choice joints and roasted them, and bringing the horn full of water from the well he feasted to repletion and lay down to rest.

Next morning, refreshed, he slew another deer and ate. (Diarmuid never ate twice from the same meal's food.) As he went to replace the horn he saw his foe again. And he spoke to Diarmuid even more angrily than before:

"You have killed two of my dappled deer, though there must be more than enough of deer in Ireland to kill. And you have used my drinking horn again and drunk of my well. This time I shall exact sore payment from you for your crimes."

They fought again, the whole day, and at dusk again he leaped from Diarmuid into the well. And on the third day it was the same. But on the fourth day, as dusk came, Diarmuid was on his guard and stayed between him and the well. And as the warrior leaped towards the well Diarmuid grappled with him, so that they wrestled long, and finally Diarmuid was plunged into the well with his foe.

Down, down they went in darkness, unending descent it seemed, until at last light burst on them and they were standing easily in another even more beautiful country. In surprise at the sight Diarmuid loosed his grasp and his antagonist made off at speed towards a group of buildings in front of which a number of warriors were practising the arts of war. One of the buildings was a noble palace and towards this the fugitive ran, right through the midst of the men at their practice. They made way for him and closed their ranks to bar the way to Diarmuid. But Diarmuid broke through them as a hawk through a flock of sparrows, as a whale through small fish, as a ravening wolf through lambs, as a mountainous wave through small boats, as a river in spate tearing all before it down the side of a mountain. And they scattered in terror and flight until he was left alone outside the palace with every door barred, bolted and guarded against him, and he weary and sore: so that he slept.

He was awakened by a light blow, and sprang to his feet, on guard. But the noble, fair young man before him bade him put down his arms, and said: "Diarmuid O Duibhne, I am no enemy. I have come to take you where you can sleep and rest in less danger than you are in here. Come."

They went to a noble house, where in the banqueting hall they were received in dignity and grace by a large company of strong warriors and beautiful ladies, all with long fair hair and clad in scarlet and gold. The young warrior then brought Diarmuid to where attendants had prepared for him a huge bath to bathe in, and healing herbs in the water soothed him and took away his aches; and rich fresh raiment was ready laid out for him when he had bathed.

He joined the company in the banqueting hall, and there was feasting and music and recital of lays and stories about the warriors and heroes of old. And though he had many questions to ask, Diarmuid forbore to interrupt the entertainment. So it was not until after he had slept and had rejoined the company next morning that he found opportunity to question his new friend. And he replied:

"This is Underwave Land. Its king is he with whom you fought at the well. I am his brother, and I spent a year with the Fian in

Ireland. I live in exile here with my warriors, one hundred and
fifty valiant men; for my brother has seized that part of the
kingdom which belongs to me, and has expelled me from the
palace. With you on my side to help me I can win back my rights.
Will you help?"

Diarmuid consented and the young king won back his kingdom.
But that is another story. Meanwhile, Finn and the Fian, after
waiting many days for the return of Diarmuid, decided to go in
search of him. And this was no easy undertaking, for no one
could climb the rock as Diarmuid had done. However, Faruach
and Foltlor contrived to make a climbing rope of all the ropes and
hawsers of their ship and themselves after long endeavour succeeded in bringing the rope to the top of the rock where they
fastened it securely. Thus the Fian came to the country of the
magic well, and here Foltlor found the track of Diarmuid, the
remains of his fire and his meals, the marks of fierce combat, and
a broken spear by the well. As they were pondering sadly on the
meaning of what they found they saw coming towards them a
horseman. He stopped beside them, gorgeously arrayed in gold
and precious stones, bade them welcome to his country and
invited them to his palace to rest and refresh themselves. They
went with him and that evening and the next day they were
entertained with the newest of meats and the oldest of drinks,
and music and song and recital of lays and stories.

At the end of it all Finn asked what was the name of the country
in which he and his company had been so royally entertained, and
the king answered him:

"This is the Land of Silk, and we are honoured to entertain one
whose name and deeds are known throughout the world. But tell
us, why are you journeying so far from Ireland and with so few
of your famous Fian?"

Finn in reply told him the story of the Hard Man from the
beginning and the reason for his journeying. The king in his turn
spoke of the great dangers of Finn's mission and offered a company of his men to help him. Before Finn could say a word of
his thanks for the offer a messenger rode up to the king of the
land breathless and in great haste. The king gave him leave to
speak his news.

"We are invaded, O king," he said, "by a host whose ships
cover all the sea around us, and who this very moment are

plundering and burning and ravaging our land. They say it is the king of the world come to add our land to his other conquests."

Immediately Finn offered his help, and the king sent out messengers to summon his army; and all marched together, and after many days of hard fighting drove the king of the world and his invaders from the land of Sorcha.

When they were resting from their grim battle a scout reported another company of warriors in sight. They came forth from the sea and Finn and his men were overjoyed to recognise Diarmuid at the head of the band. They met and embraced in great joy and gladness, and told each other of the adventures that had befallen them. And Diarmuid added that the king of Underwave Land had discovered by his magical powers that the Hard Man was really Abarta, of the Tuatha De Danann, and that he now held the sixteen of the Fian captive in the Land of Promise.

Rejoiced at last that they had news of their missing friends, the Fian held a council, in which it was decided that the best thing to do was to return to the point where they had lost track of the Gilla Deacar and make another effort to pick it up again. So back they went to the rock, and this time Foltlor found that the giant had been to great pains to conceal his track, knowing that Foltlor was with the Fian. He finally found the track, however, on the other side of the huge rock, nor did he lose it again as it weaved in and out through the islands and over the sea until they came to the Land of Promise, which Diarmuid recognised at once; for he had been there when he was young, under the care of Mannanan Mac Lir.

Finn was minded to ravage the country in punishment for the Hard Man's behaviour. But Diarmuid advised first sending an emissary to ask for the return of the captives. If Abarta refused, then they could declare war, though, he added, war with the De Danann would be no easy matter, since they were so skilled in magic.

Diarmuid's counsel was approved and Foltlor went with the emissary, following the track past every obstacle until they came to Abarta's palace, where they found the sixteen men of the Fian outside on the lawn amusing themselves in various games. Great was their delight that at last their whereabouts had been discovered, and they called to Abarta to come forth and hear the message of Finn's emissary.

177

Abarta, like Finn, was for war, but his counsellors prevailed upon him, and in the end it was agreed that the sixteen should be released and satisfaction given for the injury done. Finn and Abarta shook hands in friendship on the agreement. For three days then there was feasting and entertainment and on the fourth day they met to assess the satisfaction for the injury done to Finn and the Fian.

Finn said: "I make no claim. I thank you, Abarta, for the hospitality you have shown us, and I will give you a wage for your service as we agreed when I hired you. And let there be friendly peace between us for all time."

But Conan the Bald said: "It is easy for you, Finn, to waive claim to satisfaction; but you did not suffer as we did. I demand satisfaction."

Abarta replied: "What you ask you shall get, Conan. For I would not have your foul tongue loosed on me or my people."

And Finn was very much afraid that Conan would shame the Fian by seeking satisfaction in wealth or the like. But Conan said: "Choose fifteen of the noblest of your people, Abarta, among your nearest friends, and mount them on your brute of a horse, and yourself take the tail, and let you all journey back to where we started in Ireland, suffering the same hardships as we did. That will satisfy me."

Abarta agreed, and Finn and his men returned to Ireland to await the arrival of Conan's satisfaction. They saw the horse and its sorry burden from afar, with the Hard Man, huge, ungainly and ugly as before, running with it. Their laughter was hearty and long, Conan the Bald's jeering laugh drowning all the rest. And all congratulated Conan on the neatness of his revenge.

The Gilla Deacar came up and his men began to dismount, Finn meanwhile preparing to greet them and welcome them in courtesy. As Finn stepped forward the giant suddenly pointed to the horses of the Fian which were behind them. Finn and his men turned to look, and found nothing out of place; but when they turned back there was no sign of the Hard Man and his fifteen friends, nor were they ever seen in Ireland again.

CHAPTER XVIII

Diarmuid and Grainne

THERE came a time after the death of Finn's wife Maignes
that his companions noticed a restlessness upon him, and
they were troubled about him. For he slept little and was
abroad very early in the morning. And it was on such an early
rising that Oisin his son mentioned the distress that was uppermost
in the minds of all of them:

"What worries you, Finn, that you sleep so little and are abroad
so early?"

"'Tis that a man should have a fitting wife," said Finn, "and I
have none since the death of Maignes."

"There is no reason," replied Oisin, "why you should be without
a wife. For there is no woman anywhere whom we would not
bring you if you desired her."

"A fitting wife I need," said Finn. "But where shall I find her?"

"There is such a one," said Diorraing.

179

Oisin and Finn turned to him, their question unspoken but clear. He replied to them:

"Grainne, daughter of the high king of Erin, Cormac Mac Art. There is none in the world more fair or more fitting."

Finn pondered a little and then reminded them that relations between the high king and himself had not been friendly for some time. "It would be unbecoming for me to ask Cormac for his daughter and be refused. Let you two, therefore, go to Cormac with the request, and if he refuse, we shall be little the worse."

Accordingly they went to Tara, and Cormac postponed all his official business to welcome them and receive them with due honour. When he heard their request, he said:

"Grainne shall answer you herself. For she has refused every great hero and warrior in Erin, and it is being said that I am unwilling that she should marry. Let us go to the women's quarters now."

Cormac put the question to Grainne and she replied: "If he pleases you as a son-in-law, he will please me as a husband."

And they celebrated her consent with a great feast, and arranged that Finn should come to Tara to claim his bride.

He came and with him the great heroes of the Fian, and Cormac and the nobles of his court met them and they all sat down in order of rank and birth to the banquet.

It chanced that near Grainne at the banquet was the wise druid Daire and with him she carried on a quiet conversation about the guests.

"I am surprised," she said, "that Finn asks me for himself and not for his son Oisin, who is nearer to me in age."

"Hush," said Daire, glancing round quickly. "Finn must never know that there was such a thought in your mind. He would be insulted and reject you, and no one else would dare ask for you after him."

Grainne sighed. "Very well then. But tell me about the others. Who sits beside Oisin?"

"Goll Mac Morna."

"And beside Goll?"

"Caoilte Mac Ronain."

"And the hothead beside Caoilte?"

"Lughai of the strong hand."

"And on the other side of Oisin, the hero with the raven curls and fair winning countenance, who is he?"

"Diarmuid O Duibhne, of the winning smile, beloved of the women of the world."

Grainne went on with her questioning but paid little heed now to the druid's answers, for her mind was on a plan she had conceived. Presently she called her maid and asked for her great jewelled goblet which could hold wine for nine times nine men. Mixing a potion she filled the goblet. Then she gave it to the maid and bade her take it to Finn telling him that Grainne had sent it, that he might drink. And after Finn she bade the maid take it to Cormac and his queen and the others of his court in turn. And as they drank from the goblet they all in turn fell gradually into a deep sleep. For Grainne had mixed a drug in the wine.

When they were sleeping soundly Grainne went to Oisin and said:

"Do you think, Oisin, that Finn, who is older than Cormac my father, is a fitting mate for me?"

"Such a question were better unasked," replied Oisin. "Lest Finn should hear of it."

"Will you be my lover?" asked Grainne of Oisin.

"I will not," he replied, "for you are betrothed to Finn."

"And you, Diarmuid, since Oisin refuses me, will you consent to love-making with me?"

"No. I would have nothing to do with a woman who is offered to Finn and Oisin, even if she were not the betrothed of Finn."

"Then," said she to Diarmuid, "I put you under the great *geasa* of the druids that you take me away with you from here this night."

"Why do you choose me of all the men of Erin to place under *geasa* that spell danger and death for me?"

"Because of a day I remember. On the plain of Tara there was a great hurling match between the Fian under Lughai and the men of Tara under Cairbre. And as I watched from my window the Fian were being beaten by the men of Tara, and I saw you rise from where you sat and take your hurling stick and turn the game to victory for the Fian. From the moment that my gaze fell on you that day I have loved you and none other. Take me then with you, Diarmuid."

"I can't see why Finn would not satisfy you," said Diarmuid.

181

"And besides, when Finn stays at Tara he keeps the keys of Tara. So we cannot go."

"There is a wicket-gate to my quarters," retorted Grainne.

"I am under *geasa* not to pass through a wicket-gate," said Diarmuid.

"I believe you have no difficulty in leaping over any rampart, on the shafts of your spears. Let you leave that way. I shall go by my wicket-gate." And Grainne went to prepare for her journey, leaving Diarmuid to follow.

Diarmuid turned to Oisin. "What shall I do?" he asked.

"You are under *geasa*," replied Oisin. "You must go. And you must ever be on your guard against Finn."

"And you Oscar, what is your advice to me?"

"Follow Grainne. You cannot go against your *geasa*."

"And you Caoilte?"

"Though my wife is dear to me, I could wish I were you this night."

"And you Diorraing?"

"You must go with Grainne, even to your death."

So Diarmuid arose, and leaped the rampart on the shafts of his two spears, and followed Grainne. Again he spoke to her of the anger of Finn when he would learn what had happened. "There is not a part of Ireland we could go to this night and return without Finn knowing of it."

"There is no return," replied Grainne, "this night or any night. From henceforth we shall be together until death part us."

They went forward then in silence until Grainne said she was weary.

"I swear," said Diarmuid, "that I shall never carry you, or any woman. So let us return to Tara again now, while there is still time, before the effects of the drug have worn off."

"Let you return," said Grainne, "to the field where my father's horses are, and yoke two of them in a chariot and drive back here to me."

And so they drove until they came to the Shannon, and here Diarmuid reminded Grainne that Finn would now be following them, and that he would trace them the more easily with the horses' tracks to follow.

"Leave the horses, then," said Grainne. "From here I'll go on foot."

Diarmuid left a horse on each side of the river and walked with Grainne in the river for a mile before they came to land and headed westward. At Doire Da Both they stayed. Diarmuid cleared a space in the grove and made a soft bed of rushes and birch twigs for Grainne in the middle of it, and he made seven doors to cover the seven entrances.

Finn's trackers followed the trail of Diarmuid and Grainne to the Shannon, and across it, and then Finn knew where the fugitives had gone. Oisin and Oscar and Caoilte and Diorraing were distressed, lest Finn might come upon Diarmuid without warning; so Oisin sent Bran, the hound of Finn, to warn Diarmuid. Bran found Diarmuid asleep, and woke him. And Diarmuid knew it was a warning from his friends, who had sent the wise hound to him, knowing the affection that existed between the two.

Grainne said: "Take the warning, Diarmuid. Flee."

"There is no escape," said Diarmuid. "And I am glad. This is the settlement."

Just then he heard the three shouts of warning which Caoilte had bidden Fergoir of the loud voice give. Again Grainne begged Diarmuid to flee. Again he refused, saying that he would rather stand and meet Finn than be caught by him in flight.

And Finn came to the edge of the grove, and said: "Diarmuid O Duibhne shall not leave this grove until he pay for everything he has done to me."

Now Oisin and Oscar tried to persuade Finn that Diarmuid would not have waited for his coming but was already gone in flight. But Finn knew the work of Diarmuid in the seven doors and the enclosure he had made for Grainne; and he shouted:

"Diarmuid O Duibhne, answer me. Who is right, myself or Oisin and Oscar?"

"You have the truth of things, always, Finn," replied Diarmuid. "We are here, Grainne and I."

Finn therefore ordered his Fian to encircle the place. Whereupon Diarmuid led Grainne into full view of them, and kissed her three times, and Finn, in a great rage, said Diarmuid would pay for the kissing with his head.

At this point Angus, with whom Diarmuid had spent a time as a foster-son in training at the Bru of the Boyne, saw fit to intervene. He came on the wind, unseen by Finn or the Fian, and spoke to Diarmuid, asking what terrible thing he had done to incur the anger of Finn. And Diarmuid explained how against his wishes he had been brought to elope with Grainne.

Angus then spread out his mantle and bade them come under it on either side of him, so that he might take them far from the ken of Finn or the Fian. But Diarmuid would not go with them.

"Let Grainne go with you," he said, "and if I come out alive I will follow you. If not, bring Grainne to her father and bid him treat her well."

So they went off, and did not stop till they reached Limerick. But Diarmuid put on his battle armour, and took up his arms, and went to the first of the seven doors, and asked who was there outside.

"Oisin and Oscar his son and the men of Clan Baoiscne, all friends. Come out by this door, and no harm will come to you."

But Diarmuid sought Finn, and went and asked his question at the second door.

"Caoilte Mac Ronain is here with his men. We are ready to fight for you, and die if need be for you."

But Diarmuid was unwilling that any should incur enmity with Finn for his sake. So he passed to the third door, where stood Conan and his men, who were eager to fight against Finn; and to the other doors in turn until Finn himself answered his question.

"This is the door by which I shall pass," said Diarmuid, and vaulted on the shafts of his two spears clear over the heads of Finn and his hired warriors and away out of their view. When he was certain they had not found his track he went straight to Angus and Grainne. And her heart was in her mouth with joy at seeing him; and Angus had a meal prepared for him. So they ate and rested and at dawn Angus left them, instructing Diarmuid how he might avoid Finn's pursuit.

Thus Diarmuid and Grainne began their long wanderings, he reluctant, she full of desire for him. Going westward they met a youth, who offered his service to attend to them by day and watch by night. Diarmuid made a pact with him and he accompanied them. And they did not lack fish for their meals while he was with them; for he was a skilful fisherman. And each morn as they resumed their journey Diarmuid left a part of the fish uncooked behind him, as a sign that Finn might know, as he followed them, that he had not yet yielded to Grainne's desire for him. But the months passed quickly and Finn could not catch up with them, for they followed the instructions of Angus; and in time Diarmuid ceased to leave behind the uncooked portion of fish, for it would have been a false sign.

One morning early Diarmuid left Grainne on guard while the youth rested, and himself went to the top of the highest hill in the neighbourhood, that he might view the land. From here he saw a great fleet of ships on the water and a great host of warriors on the shore. Going down he enquired of them who they were and where they had come from.

Three of them stepped forward and gave their names, Blackfoot, Whitefoot and Strongfoot, and said they commanded the sea between Britain and the continent, that Finn Mac Cool had engaged them to capture a scoundrel named Diarmuid O Duibhne; and besides their thousands of strong warriors they had three hounds with them, whose bite was poison, whom fire could not burn, nor water drown, nor weapons wound.

"Tell us," said they, "do you know anything of this Diarmuid? Where can we find him?"

"Well I saw him yesterday," said Diarmuid, "and I may as well tell you, you won't find him an easy man to overcome."

With that, before they could ask any more questions, he asked them did they bring any wine with them; for he would like a drink. So they brought a cask from the ship, and, with everyone drinking, it was not long till it was emptied.

Diarmuid then took the empty barrel, and placing it on the top of the hill stood on it and sent it rolling down the hill and up again three times, himself all the while balanced on it.

"That's a feat of Diarmuid O Duibhne's," said he. "And there aren't many except himself can do it."

They accepted the challenge of his words. But as each man started the barrel rolling, Diarmuid put his foot in the way, and the man fell off, with the barrel on top of him, and was killed. Fifty of them were killed that way, before they stopped.

The next day he challenged them to another feat. He set his spear, the Gae Bui, in the ground, point upwards, and going back some distance took a running leap and landed lightly on it, and came down to the ground without a scratch on him. And fifty of the foreign warriors impaled themselves on the spear and were killed.

On the third day he set his great sword lengthwise between two
forked poles and climbing up walked back and forth across its
edge without hurt to himself. And as on the two days before fifty
warriors were killed, being cut in two in their attempt to emulate
his feat.

Before he left them they asked him had he any further news of
the scoundrel Diarmuid.

"Today I saw a man who saw him," he replied. "I may have
news of him tomorrow for you."

In the morning he donned his armour and took his spears and
his sword, and bade Grainne watch as usual while the youth rested.
But she was troubled when she saw him thus arrayed for battle
and he spent some time soothing her fears before he went out to
meet the foreigners.

As soon as they saw him they asked for news of Diarmuid.

"I have just seen him," he replied.

"Take us to him," they bade him, "that we may have his head
for Finn."

"His life is in my protection," he replied.

"Then you are an enemy of Finn," they said. "We will have
your head."

But with his magic weapons he wrought great destruction
amongst them and drove them back to their ships. And they
stayed there until morning. Diarmuid returned to Grainne, who
was overjoyed to see him without hurt or wound. And the youth
prepared their supper, and when they retired to rest, he kept
watch for them until morning came.

In the morning Diarmuid armed himself as before and going to
the top of the hill issued a loud challenge to the foreigners. Blackfoot answered the challenge and came ashore to do battle with
him. Nor did they use their weapons but wrestled and fought
until Diarmuid with a mighty heave threw him to the ground and
there bound him fast, so that he could not move in his bonds.
Whitefoot and Strongfoot too he bound in the same way, and
returned to the cave where he had left Grainne on watch while
the youth slept.

The youth then arose and caught three fine salmon and they
feasted happily. And Diarmuid and Grainne retired into the cave
and left the youth on guard.

Now Diarmuid had told Grainne nothing of what had happened

since he first had met the foreign warriors. But now he knew that
the savage hounds would be set on their trail: so in the morning
he related all the events of the previous days down to the binding
of the three champions.

"Did you not cut off their heads?" asked Grainne.

"No. But I left them worse off," he replied, "for no one can
loose the bonds I placed on them except Oisin, son of Finn, and
Oscar, son of Oisin, and Conan Mac Morna and the son of Lughai.
And they are my friends. However, it is time for us to move again,
for word of all this will now come to Finn." So they left the cave
which had been their happy dwelling for a time.

Meanwhile the foreigners were striving in vain to loose the three
champions from their bonds; but the only result of their efforts
was to make the bonds tighter. While they stood around in per-
plexity a woman came up and asked who had wrought the great
slaughter she saw around. Not knowing his name they described
him. She then revealed herself as Deirdriu of the Black Mountain,
a messenger of Finn, sent to look for the foreign warriors.

"This is the work of Diarmuid himself," she said. "Let loose
your hounds after him. I shall return and send Finn to you."

The hounds followed the track of Diarmuid to the cave and to
its innermost recesses to where Diarmuid and Grainne had slept,
and out again by all the places they had fled until they came to
the height of Sliabh Luachra, where they saw the fugitives on the
slope of the hill.

The first hound was loosed on them. The youth bade Diarmuid
and Grainne go ahead while he waited. He drew from under his
girdle a tiny hound-whelp and as the savage hound came at him
with jaws apart to rend him he cast the little whelp down its throat.
And the whelp went through the hound till it came to the heart,
which it tore from the body and brought back to the youth. So
the first hound died. The second hound Diarmuid killed by thrust-
ing his spear through its throat, for nothing could resist the magic
of his Gae Dearg and no magic could protect the throat of an
animal. The third hound then was loosed and he leaped in the
air over Diarmuid's head at Grainne but as he passed through the
air Diarmuid caught him by the hind legs and dashed out his
brains on a rock.

Rid of the menace of the hounds Diarmuid turned his attention
to the three leaders who had held them; and when the leaders

were slain the host fled; and Deirdriu of the Black Mountain brought the news of their failure to Finn.

Meanwhile the youth who had served Diarmuid and Grainne so well on their wanderings now begged leave to depart, and the two went on their way in great grief at losing his companionship and his service. They came to where Searbhan guarded the fairy tree which had grown from a berry dropped by accident when the Tuatha De Danann were bringing berries and fruits from the Land of Promise.

Now the effect of eating the berries of this tree was like the effect of a magic wine: they brought back youth to the aged, and exhilarated the young, and cured sickness and disease. So to prevent the people of Ireland from eating these magic berries the Tuatha De Danann placed a guard on it, an ugly giant with one red eye, whom fire could not burn, nor water drown, nor weapons wound. He could not be killed except by three blows of a huge iron club which he kept chained to him. And he was a figure of such dread that Finn and the Fian dared not hunt or travel in the country around him. So to him Diarmuid went and made a pact with him whereby he could make a dwelling for himself and Grainne in the woods, and hunt there for their food, provided only that he took none of the magic berries from the fairy tree. Here, he felt, he might be without fear of Finn's pursuit reaching him.

Finn was at Almhain with his Fian, baffled in his pursuit of Diarmuid, when there came to him unexpectedly an opportunity to continue his quest for vengeance without approaching the forbidden territory guarded by Searbhan. One day there arrived before him a band of fifty warriors, and at their head two noble heroes of comely appearance. They were strangers to all the Fian. Finn therefore asked their names and whence they came and their purposes in coming.

They replied that their fathers had been at the slaying of Finn's father at the battle of Cnucha, and had died for their deed; that they themselves were as yet unborn at the time; that their names were Ae and Angus of the clan of Morna; that they had come now to make peace with Finn and to claim their places in the ranks of his Fian.

To this Finn replied that he was willing to accept them but that first they must give him satisfaction for the death of his father.

Oisin reproached him: "Is not the death of their fathers sufficient recompense for you?"

But Finn already had a plan in mind, and refused to yield on the point.

"What satisfaction do you demand?" asked Angus.

"The head of a warrior," replied Finn, "or a handful of berries."

"It were better for you to return home," said Oisin to them, "for you know not how terrible is the satisfaction which Finn demands."

"Tell us," they said.

Oisin told them, but they could not be dissuaded; and they departed, to seek the head of Diarmuid or a handful of berries from the fairy tree. They went straight to Diarmuid and told him their purpose.

"It is a wicked demand that Finn makes of you," said Diarmuid.

But they replied that it ill became Diarmuid to speak thus seeing that he had stolen Grainne from Finn. So Diarmuid bade them choose whether they would do battle with him or go seek the berries guarded by Searbhan. And they chose battle with him. But he overcame them and bound them fast.

Now Grainne at this time was with child, and she told Diarmuid that there had come a longing on her for the berries of the fairy tree, and that she would die if she could not have some of them to eat. Diarmuid, reluctant though he was to break the agreement he had made with Searbhan, assured her that she would have them. Whereupon the two heroes whom he had bound begged to be loosed from their bonds that they might see how he would win the berries from the giant who guarded them. And Diarmuid loosed them.

Searbhan was asleep when Diarmuid went to him, but Diarmuid roused him. The giant realised what was afoot and asked: "Do you intend to go back on our agreement?"

Diarmuid then told him of the longing that was on Grainne for the berries.

"I care not whether she lives or dies," was his reply. "No one shall taste of the berries of this tree."

"And I care not by what means I win them," answered Diarmuid; "she shall have the berries for which she longs."

With that Searbhan sprang upon Diarmuid, brandishing his mighty club. Diarmuid wrestled with him and suddenly heaved him flying from the ground, at the same time grasping hold of the club. And he struck the giant as he fell to earth again three times with the club. For Searbhan could not be killed except by three blows of his own club.

Angus and Ae buried the giant at once, for Diarmuid did not wish Grainne to see him dead. When he was buried Diarmuid called Grainne to eat of the berries, as many as she wished. But she would eat none save those pulled by Diarmuid's hand. So Diarmuid pulled them for her and for himself and for Ae and Angus.

Then he bade the two heroes pull for themselves a handful to take to Finn, since that was the satisfaction he demanded for his father's killing. But when they brought the berries to Finn he smelt the touch of Diarmuid's hands on them and refused to accept them in recompense: for he knew that not they but Diarmuid had pulled them: and he knew that Searbhan must be dead; else no one could have pulled them. So he marshalled his Fian and set out for the wood of the fairy tree.

He arrived at the tree in the heat of the day and decided to rest in its shade, while he played a game of chess with Oisin. Diarmuid and Grainne were above in the thick branches of the tree, on the soft bed where Searbhan had been wont to rest, watching the game. Finn was the better player; so with Oisin were Oscar and Diorraing and the son of Lughai. Finn spoke:

"You have but one move, Oisin. If you make it you can win. If not, your game is lost."

Oisin and his friends pondered long but they could not see the move. Grainne became angry at Finn's arrogance and spoke to Diarmuid:

"Would you let Finn win the game?"

Diarmuid, without answer, dropped a berry on to the piece which Oisin must move to win the game. Oisin made the move and won. A second game was played, and a third, and in each of them the victory came to Oisin through a berry dropped by Diarmuid.

"No wonder you win, Oisin," remarked Finn, "seeing that you have the advice of Oscar and Diorraing and the son of Lughai— and the advice too of Diarmuid O Duibhne.

"And do you think," said Oscar, "that Diarmuid would remain in the tree until you came with the Fian to surround him?"

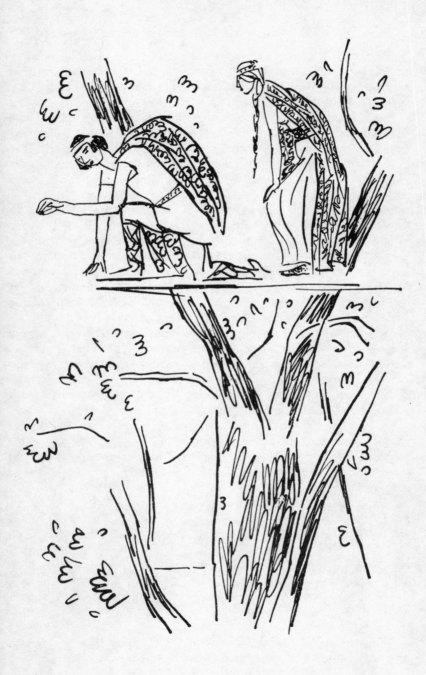

"That is what I think," said Finn. "And let Diarmuid himself say whether I am right or not."

"As ever, you have judged rightly," answered Diarmuid, and bringing Grainne forward into full view of those below he kissed her warmly three times. At which Finn became incensed with wrath and promised great rewards for the man of the Fian who would bring him Diarmuid's head.

Whereupon one of the nine Garbhs who were in the Fian, climbed into the tree to win the rewards. But Diarmuid with a kick threw him back into the midst of the Fian, and as he went through the air his shape was changed by Angus of Bru na Boinne into the shape of Diarmuid; so that the mercenaries whom Finn had brought with him cut off his head and brought it to Finn. But by now it was changed back into the head of the first Garbh. And Finn was beside himself with rage.

Each Garbh in turn of the remaining eight made an attempt upon Diarmuid, and the same fate befell them all. Oscar therefore urged Finn to call a halt to the slaughter; but he would not. Angus of Bru na Boinne then came to rescue Diarmuid and Grainne, but Diarmuid bade him take Grainne away under his cloak, and said that if he survived this assault of Finn he would join them; if not Angus was to take Grainne to the king her father at Tara and care for her.

Then he spoke to Finn and reminded him of all the slaughter he had done in the service of Finn and the Fian; and told him of the slaughter which he was now prepared to do rather than submit himself to Finn's vengeance.

Again Oscar intervened and urged Finn to make peace with Diarmuid, and again Finn stubbornly refused. And Oscar, enraged, vowed that he would stand by Diarmuid and support him against all attack. When, therefore, Diarmuid leaped from the tree, vaulting on his spear shafts, Oscar beat off all attackers until he was beyond the reach of pursuit.

Finn, however, relentlessly pursued his plans of vengeance, invoking the aid of mercenaries, both from Ireland and overseas, invoking the aid of magic, trying every wile he knew, and only after many years had passed did he realise that all his efforts must be in vain. So when Angus of Bru na Boinne came to him at last and urged him to make peace with Diarmuid he consented, though secretly nursing the hope that one day he would have his revenge.

Angus therefore arranged the peace, with the consent of Finn and Diarmuid and the high king Cormac, so that Diarmuid was to have his own district, that of O Duibhne, the district of Ben Damais, and, as a dowry with Grainne from the king, the district of Ces Corann—all these to be free of tribute, and free of hunting by the Fian. Thus was the pursuit of sixteen years ended.

Peace brought comfort and prosperity to Diarmuid and Grainne, and she bore him four fine sons and a daughter. As his daughter grew up Diarmuid gave her the district of Ben Damais, that she might live there in independence, with her own attendants. But though there was peace there was no friendship between Diarmuid and Finn, or between Diarmuid and the high king. Grainne, seeing her family grow up, was perturbed by this and one morning said to Diarmuid:

"We are rich and prosperous and powerful, yet the two greatest men in Ireland have never been under our roof. Do you not think it is a shame that we have never invited my father, the high king, and Finn, the leader of the Fian, to visit us?"

"They are no friends of mine," said Diarmuid. "Why should we invite them?"

"I should like to win their friendship for you," replied Grainne. "Let us plan a great feast for them."

Diarmuid agreed to that.

"And let us ask our daughter also to prepare a feast for them. For it may be that thus we shall find a fitting husband for her."

Diarmuid agreed to that also. And so for a full year they made preparations. And to the great feast came Finn and the seven companies of the Fian, and Cormac and his court, and the great chiefs of Ireland. A full year they spent as guests of Diarmuid and Grainne, feasting and hunting and in every kind of entertainment.

At the end of the year, on the very last night, Diarmuid woke suddenly, with a start, from his sleep, so that he roused Grainne. Frightened she threw her arms around him and asked what had woken him.

"The baying of a hound," he replied. "Is it not strange to hear a hound in the dead of night?"

"'Tis a trick of the Tuatha De Danann to entice you abroad," she said. "Give no heed to it, but sleep."

Sleep, however, would not come to him, and twice again he heard the hound before dawn came.

"I must go and see what caused a hound to bay in the night," he said.

"If you go," said Grainne, "take with you the great sword of Manannan Mac Lir and the great spear, the Gae Dearg."

"No," he said, "I need but take my little sword, and the Gae Bui, and my own hound."

And so he departed, and did not stop till he reached Ben Gulban, where he found Finn alone.

"Is there a hunt?" asked Diarmuid.

"Some of the Fian raised the wild boar of Ben Gulban during the night, and already he has killed thirty of them. I have no wish to meet him," replied Finn.

"I will meet him," said Diarmuid.

"You may not meet him," replied Finn. "For you are under *geasa* never to hunt a boar lest he be the boar that is to end your life."

"If it be, let it be so," said Diarmuid. "I shall not run before him," and he ran alone to meet him, for even his hound fled at the fearsome sight of the wild boar of Ben Gulban. Then Diarmuid said: "A man ought to take the advice of a good wife; for if I had taken Grainne's advice I would have my great sword and spear with me now." As the boar charged he cast his spear straight at the middle of the boar's head but made not so much as a scratch on him. Then he slashed at him with his sword, but the blade broke on the boar, and left him with but the hilt in his hand. With that the boar sprang upon him, so that he landed astride the boar's back facing its hind parts. Off went the boar down the steep slope trying to dislodge Diarmuid from his back, but he had to go right down the hill, and up to the top again before he succeeded. As Diarmuid fell the boar charged and ripped him open, so that his bowels and entrails burst out. But Diarmuid, wounded to death as he was, split the boar's head with the hilt of his sword and killed him.

Diarmuid was in the agonies of death when Finn and the Fian came upon him.

"It's a pity the women of Ireland couldn't see you now," said Finn to him. "They would not see the surpassing beauty which attracted them so much."

"Finn," cried Diarmuid. "Even now you can heal me, if you will."

"How?" asked Finn.

"You know how," replied Diarmuid. "At the time when you were given the gift of prescience you were also given the power of healing; so that to whomsoever you should give a drink from the cupped palms of your hands, he should be healed, even at the point of death."

"You have not earned that drink from me, Diarmuid O Duibhne," said Finn.

"Do you remember," Diarmuid answered him, "how when you were in the house of Dearc son of Donnartha, your enemies came against you, and three times challenged you, and threw fire on the house? And how when you rose from the banquet to go out against them I bade you remain and enjoy the entertainment, and then went out myself and extinguished the flames and in three fierce charges round the house slew fifty at each charge? And do you remember how pleased you were when I returned? If I had had need of a healing drink that night you would have given it gladly. Yet you say now I did not earn it."

"Do you recall," replied Finn, "what happened when you came with me to Tara that I might win Grainne, the daughter of the high king Cormac, for my bride? Before all the men of Ireland you took her from me. Did that earn the favour of my healing power?"

"You know, Finn," said Diarmuid, "that I was placed under *geasa* by Grainne, and that I would not violate *geasa* for the wealth of the world, but went with her against my will. And can you forget the many, many times when I rescued you from dire straits and from death itself, by opposing my valour and my loyalty to your danger? You have made many enemies, Finn, and retribution will come upon you and the Fian. And I grieve that I may not be there to defend you, and to defend my friends Oscar and Oisin and the rest. For a bloody destructive battle will come and few of the Fian will survive it. But Oisin will live on, to lament the Fian. These things will come if you let me die: and death is upon me."

Oscar was moved by these words and spoke to Finn: "In blood I am nearer to you than to Diarmuid. Yet I tell you at once to bring him this healing drink. And I tell you moreover that were it any other but yourself, only one of us would leave this spot alive if you were to persist in your wicked purpose."

"There is no water here," said Finn.

"Nine paces from you," said Diarmuid, "is a well of the world's purest water."

Finn went reluctantly to the well, but when he returned, the water he raised in his hands had all drained away.

"You did that of set purpose," said Diarmuid.

Without a word Finn went a second time to the well, but as he returned a thought of Grainne came to him, and he let the water flow away. And Diarmuid was breathing hard in his death agony.

Oscar drew his sword and ordered Finn without delay to bring the water. He obeyed; but when the water reached his lips Diarmuid was dead.

Those of the Fian who were present raised three loud cries of lamentation for the dead, but Finn said: "Let us leave this place now lest Angus of Bru na Boinne find us here and blame us for his death."

Four of them, Oisin and Oscar and Caoilte and Mac Lughai, took their cloaks from their shoulders and draped them over the dead hero. Then they all set out for Rath Grainne.

When Grainne saw them coming, and Finn leading Diarmuid's hound on a leash, she knew that Diarmuid was dead, and being heavy with child she fell into a deep faint. But when her strength returned and she learned truly what had happened, she sent a company of her warriors to bring home the body of Diarmuid.

In the meantime, however, Angus of Bru na Boinne learned of the death of the hero whom he watched over and cared for from infancy, and when Grainne's warriors came he told them that he was taking the body to Bru na Boinne where he would put a soul into it, so that for a short time each day he could converse with the dead hero.

And Diarmuid's sons, determined upon revenge, set out to prepare themselves for the struggle with Finn. But Finn, while they were absent, knowing of the danger to himself and knowing that Oscar and Oisin and the other heroes were against him in the matter, went himself to Grainne and though he was ill received at first, yet, such is the nature of woman, finally succeeded in winning her goodwill and in winning her as a wife.

When he brought her with him to the Fian, the heroes of the

Fian could not conceal their disgust of them. And Oisin said, "You will watch her well this time, O Finn." And the others laughed mockingly: so that Grainne hung her head in shame.

But when the sons of Diarmuid returned from their preparation abroad, they found Grainne with Finn and were persuaded by her to make peace and accept their father's place in the Fian. And there was a great feast to celebrate the reconciliation. And Grainne and Finn were together from that time until they died.

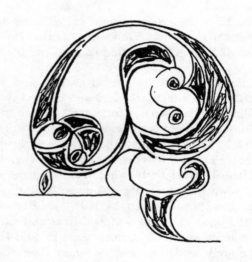

CHAPTER XIX

The Clown of the Grey Coat

ONE day when Finn and the Fian were in convention on Ben Edair they saw coming towards them a ship of war in full sail. In silence they watched until it neared land and from its deck a tall warrior fully armed rose on the two shafts of his javelins and in a bound landed on the sands of the shore. As he approached them they noted his shining armour and the brilliant red cloak which hung back over his shoulders, clasped at the throat by a fine gold brooch.

He saluted Finn and the leaders of the Fian who were present, and Finn bade him welcome and enquired of him his name and his country.

"I am Caol," he replied. "I come from Thessaly where my father is king."

Finn then asked his purpose in coming to Ireland.

"I am travelling the world," he replied, "and into each country as I come, I lay that country under tribute to me, by the power of

199

my arms. For I have not yet found a warrior to match me in any country. Now I have come to Ireland, and it is my purpose to do here as I have done elsewhere, to exact levy and tribute."

Conan Maol spoke up: "There never was a warrior yet but his match was to be found in Ireland."

"That is the word of a braggart," said Caol, "and wherever heretofore I have found a braggart I have found an easy victim of my skill in arms. But since your leader has bidden me welcome in fair words, I shall not put him or his men to the pain of death, but instead settle the matter on an easy condition. If there is among you one champion who can in swiftness of foot, or single combat, or wrestling overcome me, I shall trouble you no more."

"That is a fair condition," said Finn; "but as it happens the champion we would match against you is not here. His name is Caoilte, son of Ronan, swiftest runner of the Fian, and he is either at Tara, at the court of the high king or at Cescorran na Fiana."

"Very well," said Caol, "bring Caoilte here. Meanwhile if I may be your guest here, I can spend the time pleasantly in the company of your Fian."

"You are welcome to be our guest," said Finn. "I shall go myself to fetch Caoilte."

Finn set out at once, and his way lay through a dark wood, and here he met a monstrous clown of a fellow in a long grey coat, his legs like two masts of a ship and his ugly feet in heavy nailed boots as wide as boats. His skin was sallow and dirty and his coat was thick-spattered with mud and every step he took splashed mud over him to his head.

Finn passed no remark, though he was filled with amazement at the monstrous appearance of the fellow; but the clown spoke:

"It is a strange thing to see Finn making a journey alone with none of the Fian in attendance on him. Is there a reason for this singular occurrence?"

"I am in such difficulty," said Finn, "that I could scarce explain it to you, and even if I could, I doubt if it would do any good."

"If you do not explain it to me," said the clown, "you will suffer forever for your silence."

And he spoke so convincingly that Finn was persuaded to tell him all that troubled him.

"I know Caol well," said the clown, "and I know there is not a word of lie in his claim. And I know your cause is lost if it is on Caoilte son of Ronan you depend for victory."

"Then indeed we are lost," said Finn, "for I know not how we can match Caol."

"If you would accept me as your champion," said the clown, "I shall outrun him for you."

"I should think you would have enough to do to carry yourself and the mountain of mud on your coat, not to speak of running against a champion."

"There is no one but myself can do it," said the clown.

Reluctantly Finn agreed to accept him as champion; but first he enquired his name.

"You may call me the Clown of the Grey Coat," was his answer.

When they reached Ben Edair Caol asked Finn if he had found the champion to match him at running; and Finn indicated the clown. At which Caol shrank back in disgust, and said he would not waste his time on a race with such a dirty, ungainly fellow.

"You are mistaken in your opinion," said the clown, striding forward, "if you think you can outrun me. Just say the distance you choose."

Caol shrugged and said: "Very well. I never like a race of less than sixty miles."

Said the clown: "That is exactly the distance from Sliabh Luachra to Howth here."

"Let that be the course," said Caol.

"We shall go to Sliabh Luachra," said the clown, "if you are agreeable, and spend the night there, and begin our race in the morning."

Caol agreed and they went to Sliabh Luachra.

"We must build a house here for the night," said the clown.

"I have no intention of ever returning to Sliabh Luachra," said Caol, "and I certainly have no intention of building a house to spend but one night in it."

"Very well," said the clown, "if you give me no help in building a house, you will spend your night outside of it."

With that he went into the wood and in a short time returned with a load of timber and mountain rushes that would have built and thatched a house for ten people. He built a comfortable house with it and lighted a huge fire. Then he said:

"Well at least you will help me hunt some game or meat for our supper."

"I know nothing of hunting," said Caol, "and even if I did, I have no intention of helping you."

"Then houseless and supperless you shall be this night," said the clown, and again went into the wood and came back with a good-sized boar, which he cut up and set over the fire on spits which he had so contrived that they kept the meat continually turning.

Leaving the boar to roast, he went off again to a castle thirty miles away and returned with a table, a chair, dishes, as much bread as was ready baked, and two casks of wine, to find the boar roasted and ready for eating.

Half of all the food and a cask of wine he set aside for the morning, the other half he ate with relish and washed down the food with the cask of wine. Then he laid himself on a deep bed of soft rushes, and slept soundly and contentedly until he opened his eyes to the brilliant sun of the morning to find Caol shaking him and telling him irritably that it was time they were off on their race.

The clown yawned prodigiously and shook off the hand which had aroused him.

"Let you be off, if you wish," he said sleepily. "I still have an hour's sleep to get and after that my breakfast. Be off. I'll catch up with you." And in a moment he was asleep again.

So Caol went off in great annoyance at the contempt of the clown for his prowess, and, though he would not have confessed to it, feeling the want of supper and breakfast. But the clown slept on his full length of sleep, arose and washed, prepared his meal, ate it, drank the cask of wine and stowed the bones of the boar away in the pockets of his long grey coat, before he set off. Then his speed, in spite of his ungainly gait, was as that of a swallow, or a deer, or a March wind on a mountain top, until he passed Caol.

He halted in front of Caol and threw down the bones from the pockets of his coat.

"You must be famished with the hunger," he said. "Maybe you'd find something to pick on them."

"I'd die of hunger before I'd pick at bones that your gross tusks had gnawed," said Caol.

"Very well, then," said the clown, "you'd better put an inch to your step if you want to make a race of it." And as he spoke he was tearing off madly, and did not check his speed till he had travelled thirty miles. What stopped him was the sight of thick brambles growing on either side of the road and they loaded down with ripe blackberries. And he stayed there eating until Caol came up with him.

"Clown," said Caol, "ten miles back I saw one of the skirts of your grey coat caught on a bush, and ten miles farther back is the other caught on a bush."

"Faith, they're gone indeed," said the clown looking down; "and in that case the proper thing for you to do would be to stay here and ease your hunger with these blackberries, while I go back and collect the skirts of my coat."

"You can be very certain that is something I will not do," said Caol, and off he went.

So the clown went back and gathered up the skirts of his coat, and, sitting down, took out a needle and thread and stitched them back in place. Then off with him again, and his speed was as that of a swallow, or a deer, or a March wind on a mountain top, until he passed Caol.

"Better put an inch to your step," he shouted as he passed, "if you want to make a race of it."

Again he stopped to fill himself with blackberries, and this time when he had eaten his fill he took off his long grey coat and took out his needle and thread and sewed the coat into the form of a sack and stuffed it with blackberries. And he rubbed himself all over with the juice of blackberries until he was the same colour all over. Then off with him again.

Now Finn and the Fian were waiting anxiously on Ben Edair, and Finn was worried lest he had placed too much trust in the word of the clown. So he had posted a man to bring him word when the first of the runners came in sight. This man seeing the clown without his coat, and the coat-sack on his shoulder, ran back to Finn and reported that Caol was in sight and the body of the clown on his shoulder.

"A set of the finest arms and armour," cried Finn, "to the man who brings me better news."

At that a second spy reported that indeed it was the clown, and he had scarcely finished speaking when the clown appeared, and was welcomed joyously by the Fian, all eagerly questioning him about the race.

"Time enough for the questions," he said. "First I must eat. I want a dish of toasted corn and blackberries. I have the berries here with me. Let you provide the corn." And he emptied the sack on a great cloth spread on the green. A heap of corn was thrown into the centre of the berries.

But just as he filled his huge hand to eat, up came Caol with his sword in his hand and venomous wrath in his eyes, so that it was clear that he intended to slaughter all before him. The clown let fly at him the handful of corn and blackberries, with such force that he knocked his head clean off and away from his body. Then he jumped up, for he was seated at his meal, and threw the trunk of the body at the head with such force that it was joined again perfectly to the head—except that the head was on backwards. But before he could move again the clown picked him up and bound him fast.

"Now," said he, "admit it, son of Thessaly's king, was your mission to Ireland not a mistake?" Caol nodded, backwards perforce.

"And do you submit to send an annual tribute for as long as you live to Finn and the Fian?"

Again Caol nodded assent. Then the clown picked him up and set him sitting in the ship, and kicked the ship out to sea a full seven leagues. Nor was Caol ever seen again in Ireland. The clown revealed to Finn that he was the chief of the fairies of Rath Cruachan, and Finn and the Fian made a feast for him which lasted for a year and a day.

CHAPTER XX

Oisin and Saint Patrick

PATRICK: Rise up, Oisin. You have slept long, old, feeble man. Rise up and listen to the sweet psalms.

Oisin: I have listened to music sweeter than your psalms, Patrick, though you praise them so much. I have heard the song of the blackbird of Letterlee, the melody of the thrush in Glenascail, the cry of the hounds in the chase. When Cnu, my dear little Cnu, the dwarf of Finn, chanted his tunes and lays, we fell into sweet slumbers. When the twelve hounds of Finn were loosed through Glen Rath their cries were sweeter than all instruments or psalms. O Patrick, ask of God if he remembers when the Fian lived, if he ever saw their equal east or west of the world, or has he seen in his heaven, in conflict or might, a man as good as Finn.

Patrick: Oisin, sweet is your voice to me. A blessing on the soul of Finn. Tell me of Finn and the Fian.

Oisin: Never did we speak a lie, but by truth and the strength of our arms we came safe through every fight. There never sat

206

a cleric in a church, though sweet to you all their psalms, truer to his word than the Fian. There never sat cleric in church, O Patrick of the gentle, sweet voice, more hospitable than Finn himself, who knew no meanness in bestowing gold. O if Goll Mac Morna were alive, the swift, the mighty, or Diarmuid O Duibhne, the lover, or Fergus the poet, the king, or Daire whose singing was faultless, or Mac Garrai of the spears, or Oscar, my son, or Caoilte Mac Ronain, the cheerful, or little Ae, Finn's son, or Faolan, the gay, who never refused anyone, or Conan the Bald, or Finn's little dwarf, dear Cnu; I am sorrowful without them. O hospitable Finn, of the gifts! I am deafened by the ringing of bells and the loud chanting of psalms. O sad to me to be alive, feeble, after the Fian.

Patrick: O noble Oisin, son of the king, great in heroic deeds, tell me, without sadness, how it comes you live on after the Fian.

Oisin: Sad it must be to me, Patrick, but I shall tell you. After the battle of Gabhra, in which, my sorrow, the noble Oscar was killed, the Fian were assembled, and we saw coming towards us from the west a beautiful maiden, riding. A queenly crown on her head, a mantle of gold-spangled silk, golden her curling hair, her eyes blue, clear and cloudless, like the dew on the tips of the grass. On a white steed, on a saddle of red gold she sat, holding golden reins. She came to us and spoke to Finn.

"Long and far my journey, king of the Fian."

"O maiden of fairest form," said Finn, "tell us your name and your country, and the cause of your coming so far."

"Niamh of the Golden Head is my name, O Finn," said she, "I am the daughter of the king of Tir na nOg."

"And the cause of your coming?" asked Finn. "Is it that your spouse has deserted you and you have come to seek him?"

"No man is yet my spouse; but the love of my heart has been given to your son, O Finn, to the noble Oisin. Many a king's son and chief have given me their affection and everlasting love. But I have never consented to anyone, till I gave my love to Oisin."

By your hand, O Patrick, and no shame to me the tale, there was not a part of me but was in love with the beautiful maid of the shining hair. I spoke to her:

"You are my choice, Niamh of the Golden Head, before all the women of the world, gentle star of the beautiful face."

At once, O Patrick, she placed me under *geasa* to go with her to the Land of Youth, on her steed; and she described the land to me, its trees laden with fruit and blossom, its abundance of honey and wine, its feasts, its playing, its music, its gold, silver and jewels. And she told me that I would be ever young there, for no decay comes there with lapse of time, nor death ever. And she told me of all the thousand wonderful things that awaited me there. And best of all, herself to be my wife.

On the steed behind her I left Ireland, and Finn, my father, and the Fian. O Patrick, though my going was happy we were sad, Finn and I, as we parted. Many a wonderful day we had together, Finn and I, chess playing, and hunting, and listening to sweet music, or at other times killing our foes with vigour.

Patrick: Oisin, leave the Fian and their great deeds for a while and tell us of your journey to the Land of Youth.

Oisin: Westwards we went, and though many and wonderful were the sights I saw as I went over the waves, Niamh bade me heed them not for they were as nothing to the wonders of the Land of Youth. And indeed we passed through a dark storm of the ocean and came out of it in a most beautiful country, in full bloom, its plains smooth and fine, and in it a kingly fortress. There was never a colour that eye beheld, new gold, green, and white, purple, crimson and yellow, that was not in the royal house I speak of. There were shining sun-houses and palaces, all made of precious stones by the hands of craftsmen and artists. Three fifties of champions excelling in feats, handsome and fair, came to meet us with a noble welcome. And Niamh asked:

"Have I told you a lie, O generous Oisin? Is there anything I promised you that is not here before your eyes?"

And indeed, Patrick, no lie had she told me. The king of the Land of Youth came and took my hand and before all bade me a hundred thousand welcomes as the spouse of his daughter Niamh of the Golden Head; and he said:

"Ever young will you be here, brave Oisin. And there is not a delight on which your heart has ever pondered, that is not here in this land awaiting you."

There was a wedding feast for us that went on for ten unbroken days and nights. And thus, O Patrick, did I come to the Land of Youth and make Niamh of the Golden Head my wife.

Patrick: Continue further your tale, Oisin. Had you any children in the Land of Youth? How did you come to leave that beautiful country?

Oisin: Three children of surpassing beauty, Patrick: two sons and a gentle daughter. Niamh gave to my two sons the names of Finn, my father, and Oscar, my son. My daughter, by consent of golden-headed Niamh, I named Plur na mBan, Flower of Women, for her beautiful, loving countenance. And I stayed with them three hundred years and more before I thought to return and see Finn and the noble host of the Fian. I asked leave of the king and my wife. They gave it. But Niamh was sorrowful and laid on me the strictest cautions:

"Remember, Oisin, what I say to you, if you lay your foot on level ground, never again can you come back to me and this lovely land. If once you alight from the white steed, never again can you come back to me. A third time I say it, Oisin, my heart, if from the steed you alight, you will lose the youth you have here, you will be old, wrinkled, blind, without agility, without cheer, without run, without leap." 'Twas pitiful, O Patrick, to see her sorrowful for my leaving, as I kissed her, and my sons, and my daughter, all in tears.

I came again, on the white steed, to green Erin of the many jewels. I looked closely in every part, but found no sign of Finn anywhere. I saw approaching me from the west a great host of men and women and they came up to me. They greeted me gently and courteously, but there was wonder on the faces of all of them, at my size and my appearance. I asked them did they know if Finn still lived or any of the Fian, or why they were no more to be seen. They answered me:

"We have heard tell of Finn. There never was his equal in strength, in power, in fame. Many a book has been written by the sweet, musical poets of the Gael, about the deeds of Finn and the Fian. But we cannot tell you of them."

O Patrick, I was saddened to hear that Finn was unknown, in Ireland, to anyone. But I set out straight for Almhain, where we used to assemble in the days of the Fian, and I saw there nothing but weeds and nettles. O my grief, without tidings of Finn and the Fian. Their like was never in heaven or earth.

Patrick: O Oisin, cease from your grieving for Finn and the Fian. Greater than their like is God. By the will of God they are gone.

Oisin: Patrick, there is not in heaven or hell a place where they

209

could be held under duress. If my own son Oscar were there, no host, however great, is there that he would not destroy. Patrick, if I saw Oscar and God in wrestling grips on the Hill of the Fian, and if I saw my son down, then I might say with you that God was the better man.

Patrick: Leave your childish arguing, dear Oisin, and tell us what happened when you found the Fian gone.

Oisin: I searched every place the Fian had been, and did not find them, and as I passed through the Glen of the Thrushes, I saw a great crowd, three hundred men and more, before me in the glen. And one of them came forward and begged:

"Help us, hero-king."

I went forward. I saw a huge flag of marble and the men crushed beneath the weight of it, and they unable to move it. If Oscar, my son, had been there, he would have taken the flag in his right hand and raised it over their heads. I leaned over and lightly flung it seven perches from them. But the golden girth on the white steed broke, and I came down suddenly on the grass. The horse bolted in flight. I was old, feeble, poor and blind, without strength, without understanding, after the Fian.

Patrick: Blessings on you, Oisin. Let Brogan the scribe write down that tale, so that it may be for the men of a later time a pleasant diversion.